Contents

MOON FLIGHT ATLAS

PATRICK MOORE

MOON FLIGHT

ATLAS

Rand McNally & Company

A Mitchell Beazley Book

THE SPACIOUS FIRMAMENT

The Earth upon which we live has been carefully mapped. Every continent, every ocean and every island has been measured, and charts of the whole world have been produced. When we come to map the universe, the situation is not nearly so straightforward. There is no hard and fast standard of reference, as has been known ever since men first realized that the Earth is a globe whirling through space.

Ptolemy of Alexandria, the last great scientist of ancient times, drew up maps of the world—and also charted the sky. His star catalogue remained the best for centuries after his death about A.D.180, but it was strictly limited. All that he could do was to plot the apparent positions of the stars: he could know nothing about their nature. It was only with the invention of the telescope, in the early 17th century, that men could study the celestial bodies in real detail.

The first important astronomer of the telescope era was Galileo. Within three and a half centuries after his time, immensely powerful telescopes had probed out to distant parts of the universe; also, rocket vehicles had been sent out to our nearer neighbours in space. The direct exploration of the universe had begun.

Nature of the universe

Hundreds of years ago, men believed the Earth to be the central body of the universe, with the Sun, Moon, planets and stars moving round it once every day. This was Ptolemy's view, and at the time it was quite logical, but the modern picture is very different. The Earth is known to be a planet, moving round the Sun; the Sun itself is an ordinary star; and our own particular star-system, or galaxy, contains about 100,000 million stars of the same kind as ours.

The Galaxy is a flattened system, although seen at a suitable angle it would show spiral arms. It, too, is a minor part of the universe as a whole. The world's largest telescopes can show thousands of millions of galaxies, all of which contain thousands of millions of stars, and almost all of which are moving away from us—so that the universe is in a state of expansion.

Origins

How did the universe begin? We have to confess that we do not know. On the so-called evolutionary or 'big bang' theory, all the material in the universe was created at one moment, more than 10,000 million years ago. The steady-state theory, now largely discredited, supposes that the universe has always existed, and will exist for ever; as old stars and galaxies die, new ones are formed from matter which is being created out of nothingness. Then there is the 'cyclic' universe, assumed to be in a state of alternate expansion and contraction. If this is correct, then the galaxies will eventually draw together again, and the present systems will be destroyed, though subsequently the universe will be re-born rather in the manner of the mythological phœnix.

Of one thing we may be certain. The Sun cannot last for ever, and neither can the Earth. Life on our world must end, though not for millions of years yet. We depend entirely upon the Sun; without its energy, we could not survive.

Scale

Our Sun is a star, and appears so much larger and hotter than the other stars simply because it is much closer to us. The distance between the Sun and Earth is 93,000,000 miles—which is very great by our normal everyday standards, but is insignificant astronomically. All the stars visible in the night sky are much more remote; their distances amount to millions of miles.

On the distance-scale of our Galaxy, the mile is too short to be a convenient unit of length. Instead, astronomers make use of the velocity of light, which amounts to 186,000 miles per second. In a year, therefore, light can cover rather less than 6 million million miles; and it is this unit, the light-year, which is generally used to measure stellar distances. The nearest star beyond the Sun, a faint one known as Proxima Centauri, is more than four light-years or 24 million million miles away.

It follows from this that our view of the Universe is bound to be out of date. If a star is, say, 50 light-years away, we are seeing it not as it is now, but as it used to be 50 years ago; if the distance is 3,000 light-years, we are seeing it as it used to be a thousand years before the death of Christ.

On the other hand, the distances in our own particular part of the Universe —the Sun's family, or Solar System— are much less. Light from the Sun can reach us in 8·3 minutes, and the distance of the Moon is only 1¼ light-seconds.

External Systems

The Galaxy in which we live is not the only one. There are millions upon millions of others, at tremendous distances from us. One of the nearest is the Andromeda Galaxy, which is considerably larger than our own, and which can just be seen with the naked eye. Its distance from us is 2,200,000 light-years, so that we are seeing it as it used to be long before the start of civilization on Earth. Even so, the Andromeda Galaxy is one of the very closest of the external systems. The most distant galaxies known are well over 5,000 million light-years away.

Quasars

For reasons which are not yet properly understood, some of the galaxies are strong emitters of radio waves; also, there are the mysterious quasars, which seem to be relatively small (at least in comparison with normal galaxies) and incredibly luminous. Quasars were identified less than ten years ago, and their nature is by no means clear as yet.

Life?

If each galaxy consists of thousands of millions of stars, and if there are so many millions of galaxies, it is surely absurd to suggest that our own totally unimportant Sun is unique in being attended by an inhabited planet. It seems that life is likely to be widespread in the Universe—but the nearest intelligent beings are so remote that we cannot contact them directly, at least in the present state of our knowledge. The only possibility is to communicate by means of radio, but the chances of success are very slight. Sending a rocket to a planet moving round another star is out of the question at the moment, simply because any such journey would take millions of years. Whether we shall ever manage to get in touch with other intelligent races remains to be seen.

Other Planetary Systems?

The Earth and the eight other planets move round the Sun, as we shall see. Since the Sun is merely a normal star, there is no reason to doubt that many other stars have planet-families of their own. Unfortunately, direct proof is hard to obtain, because a planet is much smaller than a star (our own Sun could swallow up more than a million Earths), and shines only by reflected light. In the photograph shown here, taken with the

The Great Spiral in Andromeda
The Galaxy in which we live contains about 100,000 million stars, arranged in a flattened system about 100,000 light-years in diameter by 20,000 light-years broad at its centre. Our Sun, with its attendant planets, lies some 25,000 light-years from the galactic nucleus or centre. When we look along the main plane of the Galaxy, we can see many stars in roughly the same line of sight; this causes the familiar aspect of the Milky Way. Unfortunately, we cannot see the centre of the Galaxy, because there is too much gas and dust in the way, but the new science of radio astronomy has come to the rescue. A radio telescope collects long-wavelength radiations, which are not blocked out by interstellar material.

One of the closest of the outer galaxies is the Andromeda Spiral. It is 2,200,000 light-years away; it is larger than our Galaxy, and—like our Galaxy—it is spiral in form. It is dimly visible to the naked eye as a faint, hazy patch.

The Rosette Nebula *(below)*, a mass of gas contained in our own Galaxy.

world's largest telescope, every speck of light is a star. If our Sun were seen at such a distance, so that it appeared as a tiny dot, a much smaller and non-luminous body could not be seen at all. No telescope yet planned will show planets of other stars. However, a few nearby stars seem to be moving in an irregular fashion, so they are presumably being pulled out of position by invisible companions which may well be planets.

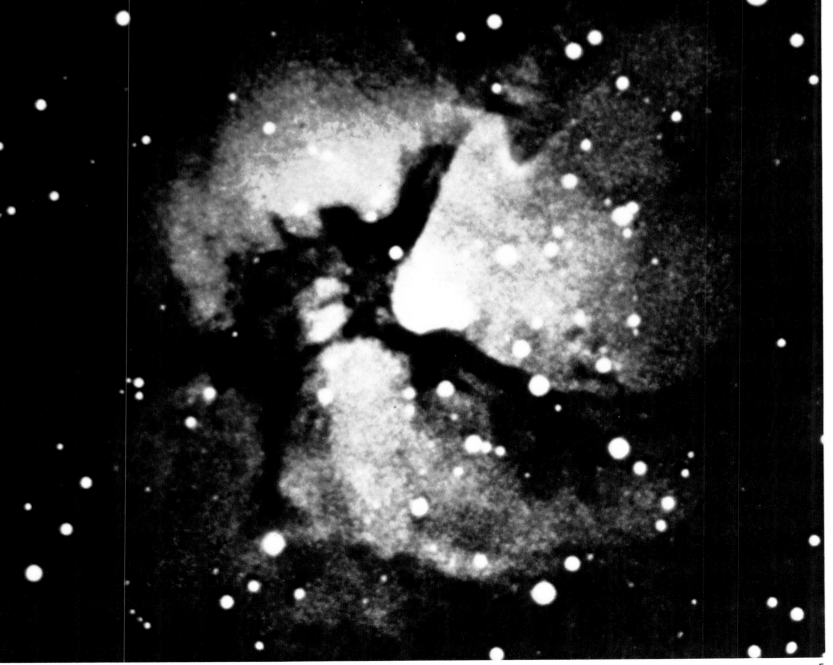

THE SUN'S FAMILY

The most important members of the Sun's family are the planets, of which the Earth is one. Some of them are attended by secondary bodies, known as satellites; we have one natural satellite—our familiar Moon—but

Jupiter, the largest planet, has as many as 12 satellites.

Also moving round the Sun are various bodies of lesser importance, such as the comets and meteoroids. Scattered through the Solar System

there is a large amount of thinly-spread material, sometimes visible in the west after sunset or in the east before dawn as the cone-shaped glow which extends upward from the horizon and which is called the Zodiacal Light.

The planets look starlike, but they have no light of their own; they shine only by reflected sunlight, and are not so important in the universe as they appear. Five of them—Mercury, Venus, Mars, Jupiter and Saturn—are visible to the naked eye, and have been known since the dawn of recorded history; all except Mercury are brilliant objects. Because they are so much closer to us than the stars, they seem to wander slowly about against the starry back-

MERCURY

Mercury is the closest of the planets to the Sun. It has a diameter that is not a great deal larger than the Earth's Moon. It has practically no atmosphere and it is quite unsuited for any form of life. Because it is closer to the Sun than we are, it shows lunar-type phases similar to those of the Moon, but very large telescopes are needed to show the darkish patches on its disk. It may well be covered with craters. A Mercury probe is planned for 1972.

☐ *Mean distance from Sun :*
　36 million miles
☐ *Year (Sidereal Period) :* 88 days
☐ *Day (Axial Rotation) :* 58.5 days
☐ *Diameter:* 3,000 miles
☐ *Escape Velocity:* 2.6 miles per second
☐ *Satellites:* none.

VENUS

Venus is much the brightest of the planets: it can even be seen in full daylight when at its most brilliant. This great brightness is partly because Venus is the closest planet to Earth (it can approach us to within 25,000,000 miles) and partly because its cloud-covered surface reflects over 70% of the sunlight falling on it. Because no telescope can see through Venus' atmosphere, little could be discovered about the surface conditions until the launching of the space probes, from 1962 onwards. The Russian probes of 1969 confirmed that the surface is very hot, and that conditions there are extremely hostile.

☐ *Mean distance from Sun :*
　67 million miles
☐ *Year (Sidereal Period) :* 224.7 days
☐ *Day (Axial Rotation) :* 243 days
☐ *Diameter:* 7,700 miles
☐ *Escape Velocity:* 6.4 miles per second
☐ *Satellites:* none.

EARTH

Earth, the third planet in order of distance from the Sun, has an equatorial diameter of 7,927 miles. It has a strong magnetic field, whereas the magnetism of Venus and Mars is too weak to be measured; and, with the possible exception of Pluto, it is the densest of the planets. Its albedo, or reflecting power, is known to be 39%, much less than that of cloud-covered Venus but far greater than that of Mars.

☐ *Mean distance from Sun:*
　93 million miles
☐ *Year (Sidereal Period):* 365 days
☐ *Day (Axial Rotation):*
　23 hours 56 minutes
☐ *Diameter:* 7,927 miles
☐ *Escape Velocity:* 7 miles per second
☐ *Satellites:* one.

MARS

Mars is always recognizable because of its strong red colour. It is much smaller than the Earth, and its escape velocity is only 3·2 miles per second, but it retains a thin atmosphere, and it is not unlikely that the dark patches on its surface are due to living material. In any case, Mars is of particular interest to us because it is the only planet in the Solar System, apart from the Earth, which may possibly support life in some form. It has two satellites, Phobos and Deimos, both of which are less than 10 miles in diameter.

☐ *Mean distance from Sun:*
　141.5 million miles
☐ *Year (Sidereal Period):* 687 days
☐ *Day (Axial Rotation):*
　24 hours 37 minutes
☐ *Diameter:* 4,220 miles
☐ *Escape Velocity:* 3.2 miles per second
☐ *Satellites:* two.

Asteroids

Mercury 36 million miles
Venus 67 million miles
Earth 93 million miles
Mars 141.5 million miles

Jupiter 483 million miles

Saturn 886 million miles

Uranus 1,783 million

THE SUN

The Sun is immensely large. Its volume is more than a million times as great as that of the Earth; it is made up of incandescent gas, and the surface temperature is of the order of 6,000 degrees Centigrade.

Telescopically, the Sun shows darkish patches known as sunspots, which are associated with strong magnetic fields.

Active spot groups often produce short-lived, violent outbreaks called flares, which emit charged particles; these particles may possibly present a hazard to astronauts, though it seems that the danger may not be so great as was once feared. Every 11 years or so the Sun is particularly active, and there are many spot-groups; the last maximum occurred

in 1968, and by 1972 the activity will be at a minimum.

It is extremely dangerous to look at the Sun through a telescope, even when a dark filter is placed over the telescope eyepiece. The only safe method is to use the telescope as a projector and show the Sun's image on a white screen. Different kinds of instruments, based on

the principle of the spectroscope, can show the prominences, huge masses of gas rising from the Solar surface. Further out comes the corona, which may be called the Sun's outer atmosphere; it is visible to the naked eye only when the Moon covers the Sun at the time of a total solar eclipse.

The Sun contains a high percentage of

Earth's nearest neighbours

Venus

In 1962, the U.S. probe Mariner II by-passed Venus at little over 20,000 miles, and sent back the first definite information that the surface is very hot. More recently, the Russians have landed three probes there: Venera-4 in 1967, Venera-5 and Venera-6 in May 1969. All these vehicles were para-chuted down through the planet's atmosphere, which is now thought to be up to 100 times as dense as the Earth's air at sea-level. The results of the Russian space-vehicles, together with Mariner II and the later Mariner V, seem to show that Venus must be a scorching hot dust-desert, with a surface temperature of at least 400 degrees Centigrade, in which case no life may be expected there. Whether manned expeditions to this planet will ever be possible remains to be seen, but certainly Venus appears to be much more hostile to man than Mars.

Crescent Venus

Through a telescope Venus shows no obvious surface detail. Generally all that can be made out is a bright disk, showing the characteristic phase: when at its brightest Venus shows up as a crescent. The markings are vague and impermanent, and represent nothing more than the top of a layer of dense atmosphere. The planet's year or revolution period is 224.7 days; recent measurements indicate that the rotation period is 243 days, and that Venus spins in the opposite direction to the Earth.
Venus showing Ashen Light, Patrick Moore 12¾" reflector. For the sake of clarity the brightness of the Ashen Light has been exaggerated.

Mars, 1969

When observed through a telescope, Mars shows considerable detail on its surface. The planet's poles are covered with whitish deposits which are usually thought to be due to a thin layer of some icy or frosty material, though solid carbon dioxide is another possibility. Much of the surface is reddish-ochre in colour, and is often termed 'desert', though there is no real comparison with an Earth desert such as the Sahara; for one thing the temperature is very much lower, because Mars is further from the Sun. On a summer day at the planet's equator the temperature may rise to 70 degrees Fahrenheit, but drops to below —100 degrees Fahrenheit during the night.

The most important result obtained from Mariner IV concerned the atmosphere of Mars, which proved to be much thinner than expected, and to be made up chiefly of carbon dioxide. The Martian atmosphere may be ineffective ground. The word 'planet' really means 'wandering star'.

There has been much discussion about the origin of the planets. It used to be thought that they were pulled off the Sun by the action of a passing star, but this attractive theory has been disproved on mathematical grounds. It is more likely that the planets were gradually built up from material collected by the Sun from space. The age of the Earth is known to be about 4,700 million years, and most authorities consider that all the planets were formed at about the same time.

The Solar System seems to be divided into two parts. The inner group of planets is made up of four relatively small worlds (Mercury, Venus, the Earth and Mars), beyond which comes a wide gap containing the small planets known as asteroids, of which the largest (Ceres) is a mere 430 miles in diameter. Jupiter and Saturn are quite unlike the Earth; they are much larger, and their outer layers, at least, are made up of gas, so that they are totally hostile to life. Moreover, they are so far from the Sun that they are intensely cold.

Beyond Saturn, outermost of the planets known in ancient times, there are three more planets. Uranus, another gas-giant, was discovered by William Herschel in the year 1781; it can just be seen with the naked eye, but it is not surprising that the old astronomers failed to notice it. Yet another gas-giant, Neptune, was tracked down in 1846 as a result of mathematical calculations by U. Le Verrier in France and J. C. Adams in England. Neptune is a large body, but it is so remote that it cannot be seen without optical aid. Finally, on the fringe of the Solar System, comes Pluto, which was discovered in 1930 by C. Tombaugh following mathematical work by Percival Lowell.

JUPITER

Jupiter is the giant of the Solar System. However, it is not a solid, rocky globe. In its outer layers, at least, it is made up of gas, chiefly hydrogen and hydrogen compounds. The most famous surface features are the cloud belts. There are also spots—in particular the Great Red Spot, which has been under observation for centuries, but whose exact nature is still uncertain. Of its twelve satellites, two—Ganymede and Callisto—are larger than our moon, and two more—Io and Europa—are about our Moon's size.

☐ *Mean distance from Sun:* 483 million miles
☐ *Year (Sidereal Period):* 11.9 years
☐ *Day (Axial Rotation):* 9 hours 51 minutes
☐ *Diameter:* 88,700 miles
☐ *Escape Velocity:* 37 miles per second
☐ *Satellites:* twelve.

SATURN

Saturn is a world of the same general type as Jupiter, but it is further away from the Sun (886,000,000 miles on average) and so is extremely cold. Its beautiful rings are made up of small particles spinning round the planet in a dense swarm. They may well be the remains of a former satellite which approached closely to Saturn and was torn to pieces by the gravitational pull of the planet. However, Saturn still has ten satellites; the largest, Titan, is bigger than our Moon.

☐ *Mean distance from Sun:* 886 million miles
☐ *Year (Sidereal Period):* 29.5 years
☐ *Day (Axial Rotation):* 10 hours 14 minutes
☐ *Diameter:* 75,100 miles
☐ *Escape Velocity:* 22 miles per second
☐ *Satellites:* ten.

URANUS

Uranus is 29,700 miles in diameter; it is therefore smaller than Jupiter or Saturn, but still much larger than the Earth. Telescopically it shows a pale greenish disk; the surface is, of course, gaseous. Uranus has a curious axial tilt so that at times its pole may be facing the Sun. The revolution period is 84 Earth years. Not much detail can be seen on its surface, but there seems to be a brightish band centred on the equator. Uranus has five satellites, none of which is as large as our Moon. Because it is so far away, it seems to be very slow-moving against the starry background.

☐ *Mean distance from Sun:* 1,783 million miles
☐ *Year (Sidereal Period):* 84 years
☐ *Day (Axial Rotation):* 10 hours 48 minutes
☐ *Diameter:* 29,700 miles
☐ *Escape Velocity:* 14 miles per second
☐ *Satellites:* five.

NEPTUNE

Neptune has been called the twin of Uranus. It is much further away, with a mean distance from the Sun of 2,793,000,000 miles and is too faint to be seen with the naked eye, though binoculars will show it. Like Uranus and the other giants, it has a gaseous surface; the colour is distinctly bluish. Of its two satellites, one (Triton) is relatively large, with a diameter of well over 2,000 miles. The other satellite (Nereid) is small and faint; it has a strange, high eccentric orbit around Neptune.

☐ *Mean distance from Sun:* 2,793 million miles
☐ *Year (Sidereal Period):* 164.8 years
☐ *Day (Axial Rotation):* about 14 hours
☐ *Diameter:* 31,000 miles
☐ *Escape Velocity:* 15.5 miles per second
☐ *Satellites:* two.

PLUTO

Pluto was discovered by Clyde Tombaugh, at the Lowell Observatory, in 1930. It is not a giant and seems to be considerably smaller than a grain of sand. Its orbit is peculiar and at perihelion, or closest approach to the Sun, it comes within the path of Neptune, but its mean distance from the Sun is much greater, and its 'year' is 248 times as long as ours; its path is tilted at an angle of 17° so that there is no fear of a collision with Neptune. Pluto is much too faint to be seen at all except through telescopes of considerable size.

☐ *Mean distance from Sun:* 3,666 million miles
☐ *Year (Sidereal Period):* 247.7 years
☐ *Day (Axial Rotation):* 6 days 9 hours
☐ *Diameter:* 4,000 miles?
☐ *Escape Velocity:* unknown
☐ *Satellites:* none.

Neptune 2,793 million miles   Pluto 3,666 million miles

the light element hydrogen. Deep inside the solar globe, where the temperature rises to over 14,000,000 degrees Centigrade, this hydrogen is being converted into another element, helium; energy is being released, and it is this energy which keeps the Sun radiating. Mass is being lost at the rate of 4,000,000 tons every second, but the Sun will not change perceptibly for several thousands of millions of years in the future. Eventually, however—in perhaps 8,000 million years, the supply of hydrogen 'fuel' will start to run low; the Sun will rearrange itself, and will go through a period of increased luminosity which will certainly mean the end of all life on Earth.

COMETS AND METEORIC BODIES

The comets and meteoric bodies are the most unpredictable members of the Sun's family. The orbits of bright comets are generally very eccentric, so that their periods of revolution round the Sun are very long; the only conspicuous comet with a period of less than a century is Halley's, which will be seen again in 1986. A comet is made up of small solid particles together with thin gas and fine dust; its motion against the stars is too slow to be noticed except by careful watching over a period of hours.

A meteor is a small particle, moving round the Sun in the same way as a planet. If it comes too close to the Earth and enters the upper atmosphere, it rubs against the air particles, and is destroyed in the luminous streak which we call a shooting star. The average meteor is smaller than the Earth. Larger bodies may reach the ground without being destroyed, and are then termed meteorites; they may be of iron or of stony material. Large meteorites are very rare, and probably do not constitute a serious risk to space-ships.

as a shield against various harmful radiations coming from space, and it is even possible that there is no life whatsoever on the planet. One thing is certain: because the ground pressure of the atmosphere is so low (no greater than that of the Earth's air at 95,000 feet above sea-level), it will never be possible for an astronaut to walk about there without wearing a full pressure-suit. Martian conditions seem to be unsuited to any advanced life-forms, and it is most unlikely that advanced life has ever existed there.

Path of Mariner IV
(right)
A probe to Mars cannot go by the shortest route; it must be accelerated from the Earth's path, so that it swings outward in a 'transfer orbit' and meets Mars at a pre-computed point.

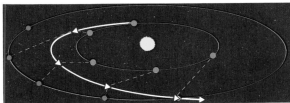

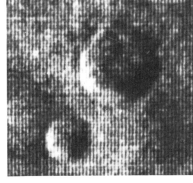

The Craters of Mars
(left)
In 1965 the U.S. probe Mariner IV passed Mars at a minimum distance of 6,118 miles, and sent back photographs showing that the surface is covered with lunar-type craters. To the surprise of most astronomers, Mars appears to be very similar to the Moon in its surface features. This photograph *(left)* is the best of the Mariner IV series.

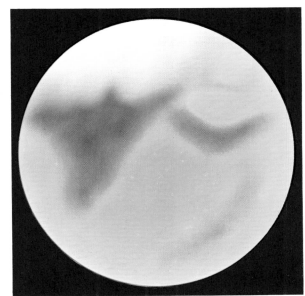

Mars, May 16th 1969 23.25 hours 12½" reflector, magnification 360, Patrick Moore.

EARTH'S NATURAL SATELLITE

A Satellite?

Apart from the Sun, the Moon appears much the most magnificent object in our sky, and we tend to regard it as an important body. Yet appearances are misleading. The Moon is a very junior member of the Solar System, and is officially regarded as the Earth's one natural satellite. Its mean distance from us is 238,840 miles : Venus, the closest of the planets, is always at least one hundred times as remote.

Yet it may be misleading to regard the Moon as a mere satellite. Its diameter is 2,160 miles, as against 7,927 for that of the Earth, so that the two bodies are comparable ; if the Earth is represented by a tennis-ball, the Moon will be a table-tennis ball. The Moon's mass is 1/81 of that of the Earth, and its escape velocity is 1½ miles per second. It may be better to regard the system as making up a double planet.

Through a telescope, the Full Moon is dominated by the bright rays which are associated with some of the craters, notably Tycho in the southern uplands and Copernicus on the grey sea-area to the north of the equator. The rays are surface deposits, and are only well seen under high illumination. The dark seas, or maria, occupy large areas of the Earth-turned side of the Moon ; there are comparatively few on the far side.

The Airless Moon

The mass-difference between the Earth and the Moon means that the surface conditions are very dissimilar. The Earth, with its escape velocity of 7 miles per second, has been able to hold on to a dense atmosphere, but this is not true for the Moon. The low lunar escape velocity of only 1½ miles per second means that any atmosphere has leaked away into space, and nowadays the Moon is to all intents and purposes airless. There may be a trace of atmosphere, but so little that it is

negligible by any standards. Shadows will be jet-black and sharp, with no air to spread the sunlight around and make the familiar blueness ; there will be no clouds, no weather and no sound. On the Moon all communication has to be carried out by means of radio, once the astronauts are out of their spacecraft.

This lack of atmosphere also means that the temperature range is unpleasantly great. At lunar noon on the equator the temperature rises to about that of boiling water, while at night it goes down to at least −250 degrees Fahrenheit. Of course, there can be no liquid water on the Moon—and suggestions that there may be underground oceans do not seem to be at all convincing. Everything we know about the lunar world indicates that there is a complete lack of life and that the Moon has always been sterile.

Our Nearest Neighbour
The Moon's distance from us is only just under thirty times the diameter of the Earth *(left)*, and it is for this reason that it must be our first target in space. A lunar journey now takes less than a week; the first circum-lunar voyage, that of Apollo 8 at Christmas 1968, was completed in a mere 8 days, where a journey to Mars or Venus and back will take many months. The Moon is our faithful companion, and stays with us in our never ending journey round the Sun. The diagram below shows the Earth and Moon to scale, at the correct relative distance between them.

The Full Moon *(above)*

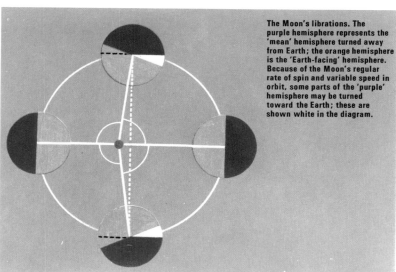

The Moon's librations. The purple hemisphere represents the 'mean' hemisphere turned away from Earth; the orange hemisphere is the 'Earth-facing' hemisphere. Because of the Moon's regular rate of spin and variable speed in orbit, some parts of the 'purple' hemisphere may be turned toward the Earth; these are shown white in the diagram.

Captured Rotation

The Moon goes round the Earth in the same time that it takes to spin once on its axis : 27·3 days. This means that it always keeps the same face turned toward the Earth, and there is a part of the Moon that we can never see. Because the Moon spins at a constant rate, but speeds up and slows down regularly in its revolution round the Earth, the amount of rotation and the position in orbit become periodically 'out of step', as it were ; the Moon rocks slowly to and fro, and the result is that we can see for a short distance round alternate edges. This, together with other 'librations' of the same sort, means that from Earth we can examine a total of 59% of the Moon's surface, though of course, we can never see more than 50% at any one moment. The remaining 41% remained unknown until photographed from space-probes, the first of which was Russia's Lunik 3 of 1959. Note that the day and night conditions are the same all over the Moon. Each day and each night is equal to almost a fortnight on Earth. Near the Moon's limb as seen from Earth, the foreshortening is so great that the craters seem to be drawn out into long, narrow ellipses, and it is often difficult to tell a crater-wall from a ridge. Before the space-probes were sent Moonward, these 'libration regions' were very poorly mapped, and not much was known about them.

The surface gravity is 1/6 of that of the Earth, so that a man who weighs 180 lb at home will weigh only 30 lb under lunar conditions. The relatively feeble pull must be borne in mind when the construction of a lunar base is planned, but on the whole it may well make matters easier! Certainly there is every reason to hope that a full-scale scientific base will be set up on the Moon within the next few decades.

Origins of the Moon
It used to be thought that the Earth and Moon once formed a single body. According to Sir George Darwin the Earth-Moon globe spun round so quickly that it became distorted, and eventually the Moon broke away, leaving the deep scar now filled by the Pacific Ocean. This theory sounds attractive, but it has now been rejected on mathematical grounds, and we may be sure that the two bodies were never one.

Either the Moon is an ex-planet which approached the Earth and became gravitationally linked with us, or else the Earth and the Moon were formed in the same manner, at about the same time and in the same region of space.

The Month
The diagram illustrates a *synodical month* or *lunation*, the 29.53 days between successive New Moons. The *sidereal month*, 27.3 days, is the time taken for the Moon to go once round the Earth: see *Captured Rotation*. Arrows align Earth and Moon with the Sun 93,000,000 miles away.

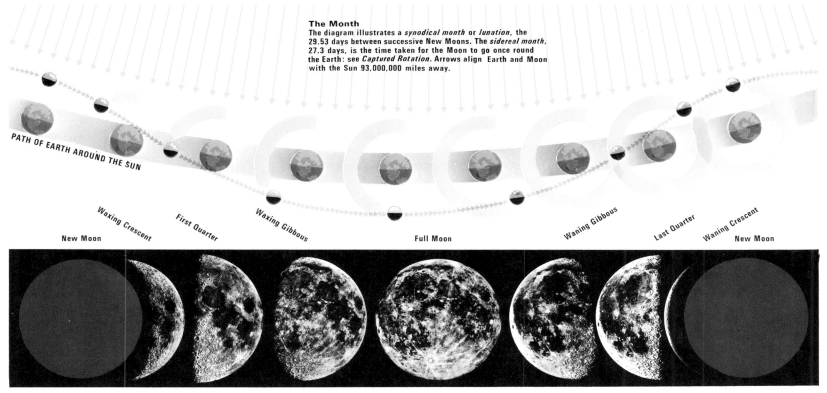

PATH OF EARTH AROUND THE SUN

New Moon — Waxing Crescent — First Quarter — Waxing Gibbous — Full Moon — Waning Gibbous — Last Quarter — Waning Crescent — New Moon

Lunar Phases

Everyone must be familiar with the Moon's phases, or apparent changes of shape from new to full. The average interval between one full moon and the next is 29½ days, so that it is approximately correct to say that there is one full moon and one new moon every month. The line between the sunlit and dark sides is called the terminator. Because the Moon's surface is so rough, the terminator is not smooth; it is irregular and broken, since the Sun's rays will obviously catch the top of a peak before illuminating an adjacent valley. When the Moon shows up as a crescent in the evening or morning sky,

the 'dark' side may often be seen shining faintly. This is due to light reflected from the Earth onto the Moon, and is known as the Earthshine. Oddly enough, the Moon reflects only 7% of the sunlight which falls upon it, so that despite appearances, its rocks are decidedly dark in hue.

As the Earth and Moon move round the Sun, it is interesting to note that the Moon's orbit is always concave to the Sun. The Earth and Moon move together round their common centre of gravity, or barycentre. This may be an extra reason for regarding the Earth-Moon system as a double planet.

Because the Moon's rotation is captured or synchronous—that is to say, it keeps the same face turned towards us apart from the minor changes due to librations—the markings on the disk always seem to keep in approximately the same positions; for instance, the conspicuous dark plain of the Mare Crisium (Sea of Crises) always appears near one edge or limb. In this and other Moon photographs in this book, north is at the top, following the American custom. (Most astronomical telescopes give an inverted picture, with south at the top and north at the bottom.)

There is almost no marked local

colour on the Moon, and the surface appears yellowish-grey, though there are many differences in intensity. During the 1950's much argument was caused by a theory that the surface was partly or completely covered with dust; it was even suggested that a landing space-craft would sink out of sight into a treacherous dust-ocean, and this idea was not finally disproved until 1966 when Russia's Luna 9 made the first successful soft landing on the Moon. The soft landing probes following Luna 9 confirmed that the Moon's surface is firm enough to support even a massive space-craft.

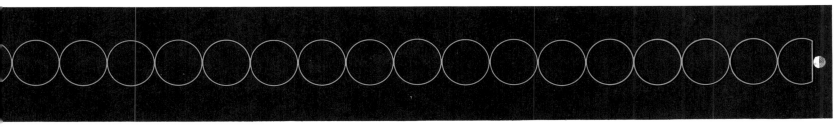

Eclipses of the Moon

Like all non-luminous bodies, the Earth casts a shadow in space, and this shadow extends well beyond the distance of the Moon. Therefore, when the Moon passes into the cone of shadow cast by the Earth its supply of direct sunlight is cut off; it is eclipsed, and turns a dim, often coppery colour until it passes out of the shadow again.

A lunar eclipse may be either total or partial; totality may last for an hour or so. If the Moon misses the main cone, it may still pass through the area of 'penumbra' caused by the fact that the Sun is a disk and not a point source of light. Penumbral eclipses are faint.

Even during totality, the Moon does not usually disappear completely, be-

cause some of the Sun's rays are bent on to the lunar surface by way of the atmosphere surrounding the Earth. The diagram, which is not to scale, shows the general theory of a lunar eclipse, which is quite straightforward.

Lunar eclipses are particularly interesting because as soon as the direct sunlight is cut off, a wave of

intense cold sweeps across the Moon's surface. There is no atmosphere to blanket in any warmth, and the lunar surface materials are very poor at retaining heat, so the temperature drops very sharply. Some areas, notably the great ray-crater Tycho, cool down less rapidly than their surroundings and have been called 'hot spots'.

Lunar eclipses are not really important, but they are interesting to watch; the Earth's shadow is impressive as it creeps slowly across the Moon's disk. Because the Moon's orbit is inclined by 5° to that of the Earth, eclipses do not occur every month. For obvious reasons, a lunar eclipse can take place only at Full Moon. Any place on Earth will see several lunar eclipses in each decade.

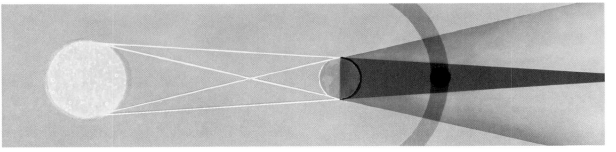

(left) A diagram showing the theory of Lunar Eclipse (not to scale).

FEATURES OF THE MOON

The Moon's appearance alters very much according to the angle of illumination. When the Sun is high over a crater, there are almost no shadows, and the crater may be hard to find; yet when the formation is close to the terminator, or boundary between the sunlit and light hemispheres of the Moon, its floor is shadow-covered, and the crater stands out magnificently.

Bright and Dark Craters

There are a few craters which may be recognized easily under any conditions of illumination. Aristarchus is one of these, because it is so bright; it may even be made out when on the night side, shining by reflected Earthlight. Another crater which can never be mistaken is Plato, in the region of the Mare Imbrium (Sea of Showers), whose floor is extremely dark, and looks remarkably smooth when seen through a telescope. Generally speaking, however, the Moon looks at its most spectacular when in the crescent, half or gibbous stage; when full, the details are hard to make out, and the bright rays from a few craters such as Tycho and Copernicus dominate the lunar landscape, masking other features.

Colour of the Moon

There is to all intents and purposes no local colour on the Moon striking enough to be visible through a telescope. For this reason, most lunar photographs taken from Earth-based observatories are in black and white. However, colour pictures can be quite spectacular. The view given here was taken by Henry Brinton with his 12-inch reflecting telescope at his private observatory in Sussex. The colour rendering is realistic; the Moon is yellowish, and the shadows are inky black. It is rather surprising to find that the lunar rocks reflect, on average, only about 7% of the sunlight which falls upon them.

Moderate telescopes will show immense detail on the Moon. The world's largest telescopes are almost never used for lunar work, but in any case the use of a giant instrument would not give so much advantage as might be expected. The black and white photographs given on these pages were also taken with a 12-inch reflector; they are the work of Commander H. R. Hatfield, R.N., also from a private observatory in Sevenoaks in Southern England.

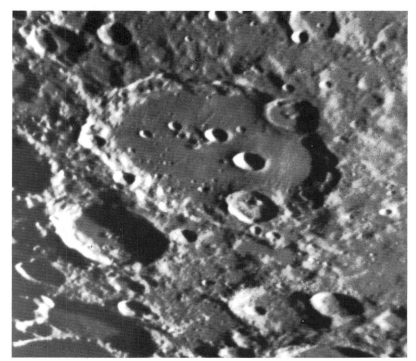

Clavius (left)
The great crater Clavius, which is more than 140 miles in diameter, has massive, fairly regular walls. Inside it are several smaller craters. Clavius is one of the largest craters on the Moon. (Map: 35 and 39)

The Straight Wall (Rupes Recta) (right)
The so-called Straight Wall, in the centre of the picture, lies at the edge of the Mare Nubium (Sea of Clouds). It is not a wall: it is in fact a fault, 80 miles long and 800 feet high, with a slope of about 40°. (Map: 29)

Triesnecker (far right)
Near the Sinus Medii (Central Bay)—the alternative landing site selected for Apollo 11. The crater near the centre is Triesnecker; to the right may be seen a complex system of clefts or rilles, which are cracks in the lunar surface. The Hyginus Cleft is to the upper right of Triesnecker, and the craters Godin and Agrippa are to be seen in the uplands to the lower right. (Map: 18)

All the photographs are printed with north at the top.

The Half Moon (right)

The Half-moon, photographed in colour by Henry Brinton with the 12-inch reflector at his private observatory at Selsey. This half of the Moon includes the Apollo 11 landing-site. The conspicuous little 'sea' close to the limb is the Mare Crisium, or Sea of Crises; this is also shown in the photographs taken by the astronauts of Apollo 8 and Apollo 10, and is a prominent landmark. The Mare Tranquillitatis (Sea of Tranquillity), Apollo II's landing site, is also well shown. Adjoining the Mare Tranquillitatis is the well-formed Mare Serenitatis (Sea of Serenity) in the northern hemisphere of the Moon. To the south are the rugged lunar uplands, where craters of all sizes abound; they break into each other, and there seems to be almost no level ground. Neither is there any well-marked local colour on the Moon; as the photograph shows, the prevalent hue is yellowish-grey.

All the features shown on this photograph may be seen with the aid of a comparatively small astronomical telescope. Note the shadows in the craters near the terminator, i.e. the line between the daylit and night sides of the Moon.

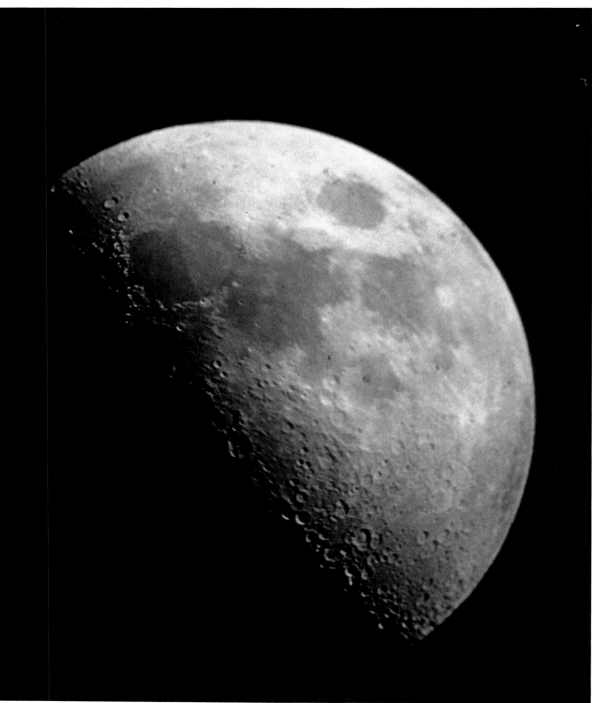

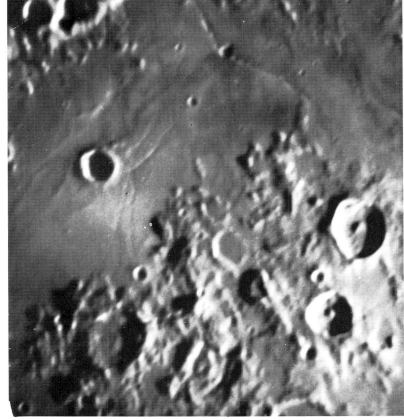

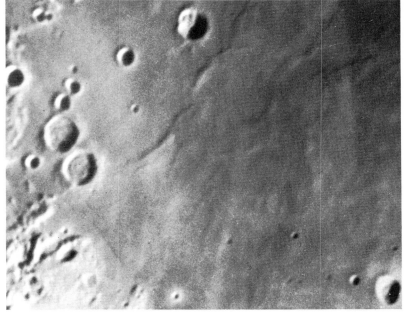

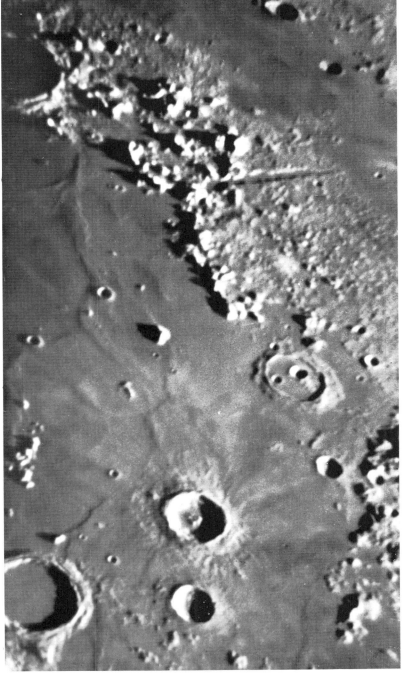

The Landing Site (*above*)
The Mare Tranquillitatis or Sea of Tranquillity—the landing site of Apollo 11, which was photographed in detail by Apollo 10. This view, taken from Earth, shows the twin craters Sabine and Ritter, left of centre ; Maskelyne lies to the lower right, and Möltke is the small bright crater at the bottom of the pnotograph, towards the centre. (Map : 19)

The Alps (*right*)
The mountain range of the Alps, on the border of the Mare Imbrium, cut through by the famous 80-mile valley. To the bottom left of the photograph lies Archimedes, a regular 50-mile crater with a comparatively smooth floor. (Map : 5 & 6) The Alps contain some lofty peaks, the highest of which rise to some 12,000 feet above general surface level.

Theophilus (*below*)
Enlarged view of the majestic 64-mile crater Theophilus, with its high central peak. The walls rise to 18,000 feet above the lowest part of the floor. Adjoining Theophilus, and slightly deformed by it, is Cyrillus ; below Cyrillus is the third member of the trio, Catharina, which is less perfect. The great plain to the lower right of Theophilus is the Mare Nectaris (Sea of Nectar). (Map : 25)

MAPPING THE MOON

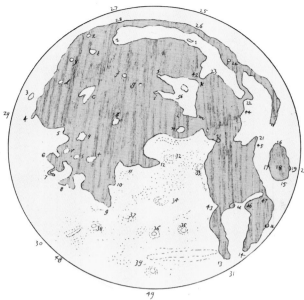

Newton's Reflector

Harriot, 1609
Telescopes were invented during the first years of the 17th century, and in 1610 the great Italian astronomer Galileo used a telescope to make a map of the Moon, although a few months earlier a chart had been drawn by Thomas Harriot, one-time tutor to Raleigh. Harriot, like Galileo, drew the main craters, together with the broad dark plains which were then thought to be seas of open water.

Patrick Moore's Observatory

Humboldt from Earth, 1967
As telescopes became more powerful, better maps were made. Then came photographs to reveal the lunar surface in great detail, from which really accurate maps could be compiled but Earth-based photography has its limitations. The great crater Wilhelm Humboldt (*left*) appears as a narrow ellipse. (Map: 32).

Orbiter

Humboldt from Orbiter 4, 1967
Moon-mapping made great strides in the mid-1960's, with the flights of the American Orbiter probes. By 1967 the mapping of the Moon's surface had been revolutionized. Wilhelm Humboldt is seen (*left*) at a distance of only a few tens of miles. Humboldt is seen here 'from above', so that it is no longer foreshortened. (Map: 32)

Luna 9

First Photograph from Lunar Surface, 1966
Between 1964 and 1965 the Americans' Ranger probes crash-landed on the lunar surface, but during the last minutes of flight sent back close-range pictures of the Moon. In 1966 the Russians' Luna 9 landed gently in Oceanus Procellarum (Ocean of Storms). (Map: 15, 21 and 22)

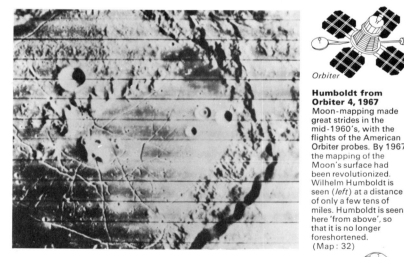

Moon's surface

At a first glance, the Moon's surface appears to be so crowded with detail that it seems almost impossible to tell one feature from another. There are thousands of craters, as well as the wide dry plains still miscalled 'seas'; there are mountain ranges, isolated peaks, valleys, and minor features such as the crack-like rilles or clefts. When the Moon is near full, the bright rays centred upon a few of the craters, notably Tycho in the southern hemisphere, dominate the whole scene, and make even large craters hard to identify.

Much depends upon the Moon's phase. A crater lying near the terminator or boundary between the daylit and night hemispheres, will be partly or wholly filled with shadow, and will be very prominent. Later, when the terminator has passed on and the crater is fully illuminated, there will be little or no interior shadow—and the crater may

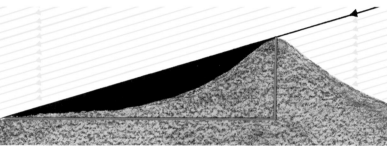

Measuring Lunar Heights
The shadows of the mountains and the crater-walls alter quickly with the changing illumination, and a feature which is prominent on one night may be almost invisible on the next.

The lengths of the shadows on to the ground below provide the best means of measuring the heights of the elevations, as was originally done by Galileo more than 350 years ago.

be hard to find, even if it is large and deep. There are some craters which always stand out, either because their floors are very dark or else because of their bright walls, but generally speaking it is not easy to identify many of the surface formations around the time of full moon. The best time to observe is when the phase is half, crescent or three-quarter.

Some system of naming the features had to be found, So far as the craters are concerned, the system in use today is based upon that of Riccioli, an Italian Jesuit who drew a fairly good map of the Moon as long ago as 1651. Riccioli named the principal craters in honour of famous scientists, such as Tycho, Copernicus and Ptolemy. The system has been retained and extended, and nowadays hundreds of names are accepted by the International Astronomical Union. The mountains are sometimes named after Earth ranges; thus we have the lunar Apennines, Alps, Caucasus and Taurus. The names of the 'seas' are romantic; among them may be cited the Mare Crisium (Sea of Crises), Mare Imbrium (Sea of Showers), Oceanus Procellarum (Ocean of Storms), Sinus Iridum (Bay of Rainbows) and, of course, the Mare Tranquillitatis (Sea of Tranquillity), containing one landing-site for the first manned expedition to the Moon.

Although the differing illumination produces quick apparent changes, the surface features of the Moon do not change from one century to another. The craters, mountains and valleys look the same now as they must have done for millions of years; there are no large-scale disturbances of the crust, and in the absence of atmosphere there is no wind or water to wear away the lunar peaks. Erosion, in fact, does not occur.

We have no certain evidence that there have been any changes on the Moon since the first good maps were

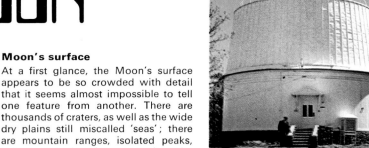

Dome of Lowell Refractor
Dome of the 24-inch Lowell refractor at Flagstaff, in Arizona, once used for studying Mars, and more recently used in drawing up the official American maps of the Moon.

drawn up. On the other hand, there are occasional reddish glows known as transient lunar phenomena (TLPs for short). Amateur observers reported them on many occasions before the start of the Space Age, and they have since been seen by professional observers also. Some, for example, have been reported by observers at the Lowell Observatory at Flagstaff, in Arizona, where Moon-mapping was carried out in the early 1960's with the help of a very powerful telescope.

The exact nature of these reddish glows is not known. Some astronomers regard them as gaseous emissions from below the Moon's crust, in which case it would seem that there is a certain amount of small-scale volcanic activity still going on. Also, studies of the movements of rockets put into orbits round the Moon have shown that some of the circular 'seas' are associated with masses of heavy material, known as mascons (from *mass concentrations*). The nature of the mascons is uncertain, but they have to be taken into account, because their attractions are strong enough to cause measurable disturbances in the paths of rocket vehicles travelling near the Moon.

For more than twenty years it has been possible to bounce radar waves off the Moon, and information has been obtained with regard to the nature of the surface layers. The sub-surface temperature is relatively uniform.

The Craters of the Moon

The lunar craters may be of great size—far larger than any well-formed craters on the Earth. Yet a lunar crater cannot be compared with a deep, steep-sided well or mine-shaft; seen in profile, it is more like a shallow saucer. A large crater may have a central mountain, or group of mountains; in other cases there is no central elevation of any kind, though the floor may contain many smaller craters and other features. In some craters there is much detail.

When a lunar crater is seen near the terminator, with its floor covered with black shadow, it certainly looks very deep—but appearances are deceptive. A typical crater has a wall which rises to a moderate height above the outer country; the floor is sunken, and the central peak never rises to the height of the outer rampart. The deepest craters on the Moon have floors which are well over 10,000 feet below the wall-crests, but all these are large formations, so that the relative depths are not very great. Moreover, the slopes of the walls are usually gentle.

The mountains are comparatively high, and rise in some cases to well over 20,000 feet. Absolute comparisons with Earth mountains are not easy to make, because there is no water on the Moon and so heights of peaks cannot be related to sea-level; but many of the crests are very lofty indeed. On the other hand, the mountain ranges are not basically similar to those of the Earth; usually, the peaks form the boundaries of the wall-marked circular seas or maria. Isolated peaks and groups of peaks also occur, even on the floors of the seas.

Origin of Craters

There has been a great deal of argument about the origin of the Moon's craters. Some astronomers believe them to be volcanic structures of the kind known as calderas; others consider them as having been produced by the impacts

Crater Sizes
Size of the lunar crater Clavius, compared with England. The diameter is 146 miles; the walls are regular and massive. No well-formed terrestrial crater rivals Clavius in size. (Map: 35 and 39)

of meteorites. Both kinds of structures exist on Earth, as shown here, Crater Lake, Oregon, is volcanic, while the Meteor Crater in Arizona is of impact origin—each being rather less than 1 mile in diameter. No doubt both volcanic and impact craters are to be found on the Moon. Direct exploration of the lunar surface will probably clear the matter up.

Inside a Crater

If an astronaut landed inside a large lunar crater, he would have no sensation of being shut in by towering walls! Indeed, if he landed in near the centre of one of the great formations he would be unable to see the walls at all, since they would be below his horizon. The Moon is much smaller than the Earth, and its surface curves more sharply, so that the horizon will be only about 1½ miles from an observer who is standing on level ground. The walls and central elevations of a really large crater would not be quickly recognizable to an observer on the surface; they would seem to be much less marked than local irregularities such as pits, mounds and minor hills.

Rough Uplands (right)
The rough uplands closely outside the crater Tycho, as photographed by the American lunar probe Surveyor 7. There is almost no level ground here. (Map: 35)

Height of Lunar Mountains (below)
Heights of some of the loftiest lunar mountains, compared with Mont Blanc. Relatively, as well as absolutely, the Moon's peaks surpass those of Earth.

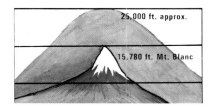

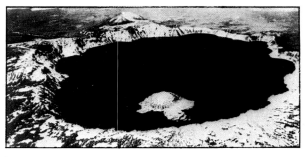

Crater Lake, Oregon
This is a volcanic caldera, whose floor is now hidden because the crater is partly filled with water. It has suffered some erosion.

Meteor Crater, Arizona
Photograph of the Meteor Crater in Arizona, which is almost 1 mile in diameter, and was produced by a meteoritic impact thousands of years ago.

Crater Profile (above)
Profile of the lunar crater Alphonsus, which is 70 miles in diameter and has fairly regular walls. Though the floor is depressed below the crest of the wall, the crater is not deep relative to its diameter; indeed, its profile is more like a shallow saucer than a mine-shaft. This is typical of all the large craters of the Moon.

Alphonsus (below)
A photograph of the interior of Alphonsus, taken from the American Ranger 9 in 1965. Shortly after this photograph was taken, Ranger 9 crash-landed inside the crater. (Map: 23)

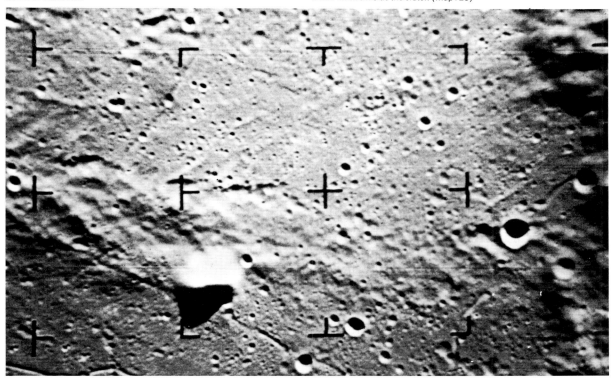

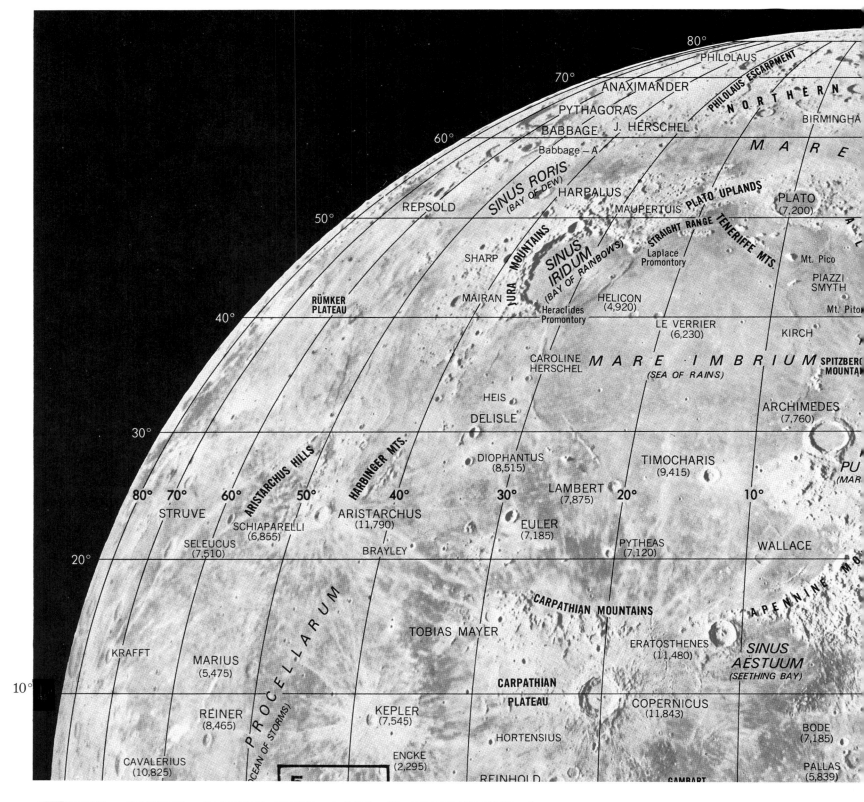

Map labels (Atlas of the Moon):

80°
PHILOLAUS
70° ANAXIMANDER
PYTHAGORAS N O R T H E R N
BABBAGE J. HERSCHEL PHILOLAUS ESCARPMENT BIRMINGHA
60° Babbage — A M A R E
SINUS RORIS HARPALUS PLATO UPLANDS
REPSOLD (BAY OF DEW) MAUPERTUIS PLATO
50° (7,200)
SHARP JURA MOUNTAINS SINUS STRAIGHT RANGE TENERIFFE MTS. Mt. Pico
RÜMKER IRIDUM Laplace PIAZZI
PLATEAU MAIRAN (BAY OF RAINBOWS) Promontory SMYTH
40° HELICON Mt. Pito
Heraclides (4,920) LE VERRIER KIRCH
Promontory (6,230)
CAROLINE M A R E I M B R I U M SPITZBERG
HERSCHEL (SEA OF RAINS) MOUNTAI
HEIS ARCHIMEDES
DELISLE (7,760)
30°
DIOPHANTUS TIMOCHARIS PU
ARISTARCHUS HILLS HARBINGER MTS. (8,515) (9,415) (MAR
80° 70° 60° 50° 40° 30° LAMBERT 20° 10°
STRUVE ARISTARCHUS (7,875)
SCHIAPARELLI (11,790) EULER WALLACE
SELEUCUS (6,855) (7,185) PYTHEAS
(7,510) BRAYLEY (7,120)
20°
P R O C E L L A R U M CARPATHIAN MOUNTAINS A P E N N I N E M
KRAFFT TOBIAS MAYER ERATOSTHENES SINUS
MARIUS (11,480) AESTUUM
10° (5,475) CARPATHIAN (SEETHING BAY)
(OCEAN OF STORMS) PLATEAU COPERNICUS
REINER KEPLER (11,843) BODE
(8,465) (7,545) (7,185)
HORTENSIUS
CAVALERIUS ENCKE PALLAS
(10,825) (2,295) (5,839)
REINHOLD GAMBART

ATLAS OF THE MOON 1 : 7600000

What to see: Northern Area

The northern part of the Moon's Earth-turned hemisphere contains two of the most perfect of the waterless seas, the Mare Imbrium (Sea of Showers) and the Mare Serenitatis (Sea of Serenity). Both are very large; the Mare Serenitatis covers 125,000 square miles, an area slightly more than that of Great Britain, while the Mare Imbrium is as extensive as Britain and France put together. Further north is the irregular, patchy Mare Frigoris or Sea of Cold.

The Bay of Rainbows

One of the most beautiful of all the lunar features is the Sinus Iridum (Bay of Rainbows), which leads off the Mare Imbrium. Its mountainous border can sometimes catch the sunlight when the

Moon is between half and full, so that the Bay seems to stand out from the rest of the disk. Bounding the Mare Imbrium are two of the most majestic of all the lunar ranges, the Apennines, rising in places to over 15,000 feet, and the Alps, which are cut through by the magnificent and unique valley (Vallis Alpina) over 80 miles long.

Of the craters, special mention should be made of Plato, which is 60 miles in diameter and lies near the edge of the Mare Imbrium. It is almost perfectly circular, though as seen from Earth it appears foreshortened into an ellipse. Its dark floor makes it recognizable under any conditions of lighting, and inside it many observers have reported temporary local obscurations, perhaps due to gases seeping out from below the Moon's crust. Even more interesting is Aristarchus, which is the brightest crater on the entire Moon. It

lies on the vast Oceanus Procellarum or Ocean of Storms, and can often be seen when lit only by Earthshine; on more than one occasion it has been mistaken for a volcano in eruption. Reddish glows have frequently been seen in and near it, and it is also close to a magnificent winding valley, associated with the adjacent crater Herodotus. This valley, known as Schröter's Valley in honour of its discoverer, is a splendid sight in a small telescope when suitably illuminated.

The Archimedes Group

There are many other imposing craters in the northern part of the Moon, notably the 50-mile Archimedes, which is one of the most conspicuous objects on the floor of the Mare Imbrium. Archimedes has a relatively flat floor, but its two companions, Aristillus and Autolycus, are deeper and peaked.

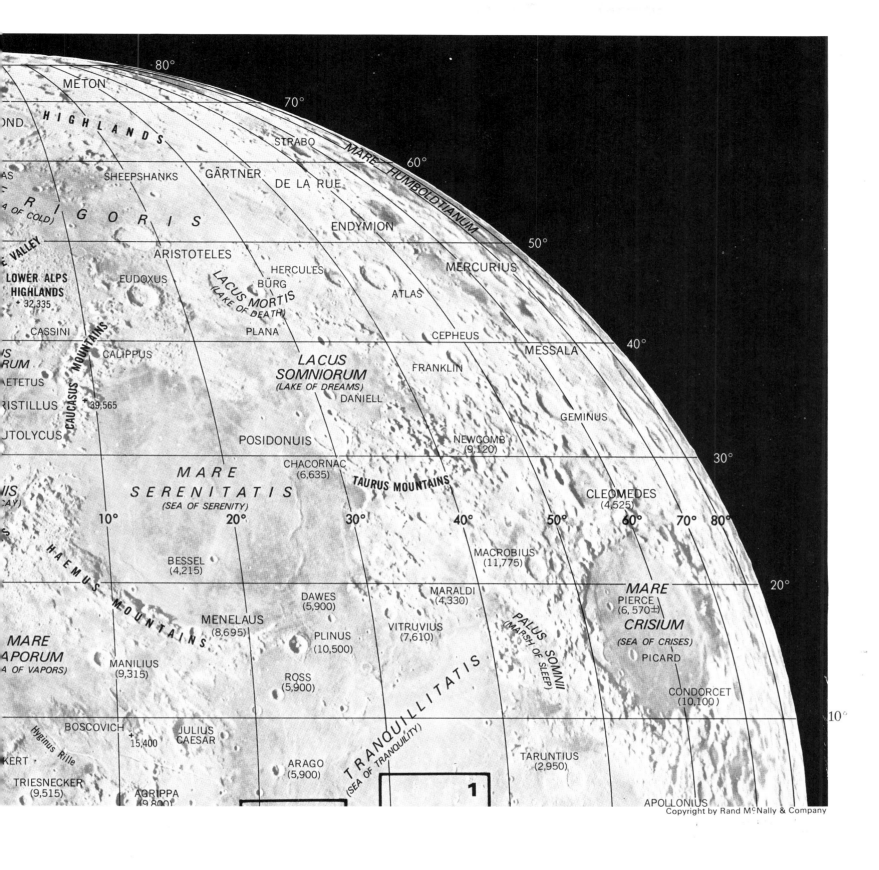

METON
HIGHLANDS
80°
70°
STRABO
MARE HUMBOLDTIANUM
60°
SHEEPSHANKS GÄRTNER DE LA RUE
FRIGORIS
(OF COLD)
ENDYMION
50°
LOWER ALPS HIGHLANDS
+ 32,335
ARISTOTELES
EUDOXUS
HERCULES
BÜRG
LACUS MORTIS
(LAKE OF DEATH)
ATLAS
MERCURIUS
VALLEY
CASSINI
PLANA
CEPHEUS
40°
CALIPPUS
MESSALA
CAUCASUS MOUNTAINS
+ 39,565
FRANKLIN
LACUS SOMNIORUM
(LAKE OF DREAMS)
DANIELL
GEMINUS
RISTILLUS
UTOLYCUS
POSIDONUIS
NEWCOMB
(9,120)
30°
CHACORNAC
(6,635)
MARE SERENITATIS
(SEA OF SERENITY)
TAURUS MOUNTAINS
CLEOMEDES
(4,525)
10° 20° 30° 40° 50° 60° 70° 80°
HAEMUS MOUNTAINS
BESSEL
(4,215)
MACROBIUS
(11,775)
20°
DAWES
(5,900)
MARALDI
(4,330)
MARE CRISIUM
(SEA OF CRISES)
PIERCE
(6,570±)
MARE VAPORUM
(A OF VAPORS)
MENELAUS
(8,695)
PLINUS
(10,500)
VITRUVIUS
(7,610)
PALUS SOMNII
(MARSH OF SLEEP)
PICARD
MANILIUS
(9,315)
ROSS
(5,900)
CONDORCET
(10,100)
BOSCOVICH
+ 15,400
JULIUS CAESAR
Hyginus Rille
TRANQUILLITATIS
(SEA OF TRANQUILITY)
TARUNTIUS
(2,950)
10°
TRIESNECKER
(9,515)
AGRIPPA
(9,800)
ARAGO
(5,900)
1
APOLLONIUS

Copyright by Rand McNally & Company

INDEX

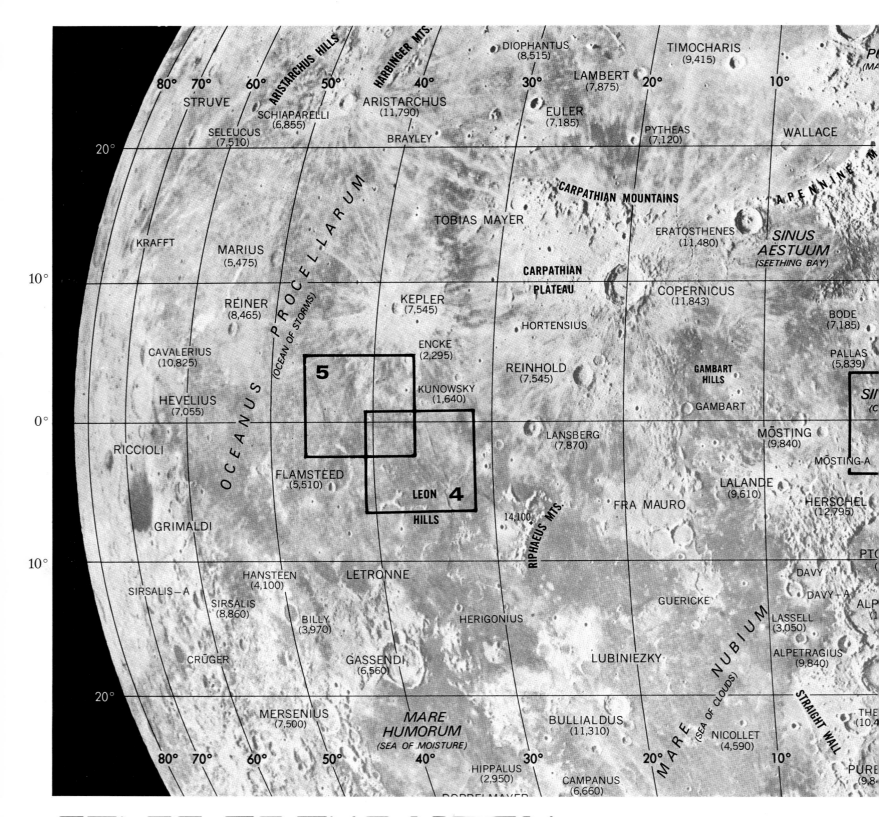

ATLAS OF THE MOON

1 : 7600000

What to see: Central Area

The central part of the Moon contains some of the grey, waterless 'seas' as well as some majestic craters. Copernicus, in particular, stands out. It is a huge enclosure 56 miles in diameter, with walls rising well over 10,000 feet above the lowest part of a floor which contains a central mountain group; the walls are beautifully terraced. When it is seen under high illumination, Copernicus shows up magnificently, because it is the centre of a system of bright streaks or rays. Another ray-centre is the smaller crater Kepler, in the Oceanus Procellarum (Ocean of Storms). Much closer to the Moon's edge as seen from Earth are two very large craters, Grimaldi and Riccioli, whose dark floors make them very easy

to identify. Another very interesting crater is Gassendi, on the border of the Mare Humorum (Sea of Humours) which lies in the third section of this map.

The Ptolemæus Group

The Mare Nubium (Sea of Clouds) contains many ruined craters. Close to the centre of the Moon's Earth-turned face is a splendid group of walled plains, Ptolemæus, Alphonsus and Arzachel, which are prominent in this section of the map. Ptolemæus, over 90 miles across, has a relatively flat floor; Alphonsus has a central mountain group, and is notable because of the reddish patches occasionally seen inside it. Further east lie Theophilus and its companions; Theophilus is one of the best-formed and deepest craters on the whole Moon.

The Mare Tranquillitatis (Sea of Tranquillity) is the area which was surveyed at close range by the three astronauts of Apollo 10 in May 1969. The selected landing-site for Apollo 11, near the crater Möltke, was observed from a height of less than 10 miles. Observations were also made of the alternative landing-site, in the Sinus Medii (Central Bay), near the crater Bruce.

Other features of particular interest are the clefts or rilles (rimæ) associated with Hyginus and Ariadæus; the grey Mare Fœcunditatis (Sea of Fertility) with its twin craterlets Messier and Messier A; and the large crater Langrenus, which was beautifully photographed by the Apollo 8 astronauts in December 1968. The well-marked Mare Crisium (Sea of Crises) also lies partly in this section; it is clearly visible with the naked eye.

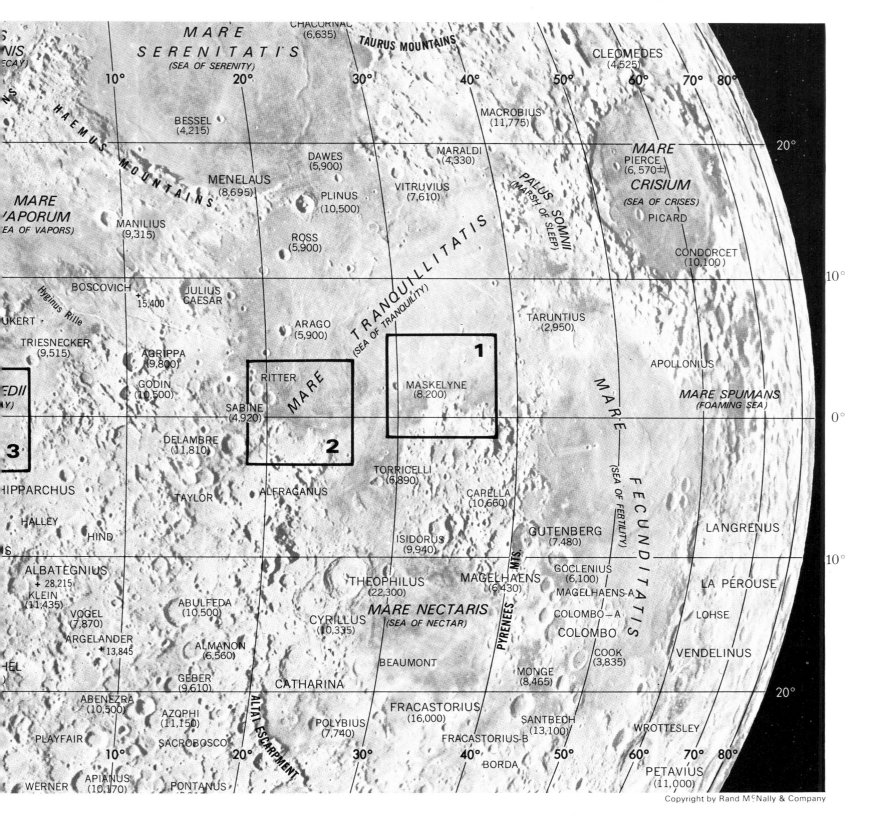

MARE
SERENITATIS
(SEA OF SERENITY)

CHACORNAC
(6,635)

TAURUS MOUNTAINS

CLEOMEDES
(4,525)

10°   20°   30°   40°   50°   60°   70° 80°   20°

BESSEL
(4,215)

MACROBIUS
(11,775)

MARALDI
(4,330)

MARE
PIERCE
(6,570±)

MARE
VAPORUM
(SEA OF VAPORS)

MENELAUS
(8,695)

DAWES
(5,900)

VITRUVIUS
(7,610)

PALUS SOMNII
(MARSH OF SLEEP)

CRISIUM
(SEA OF CRISES)

PICARD

MANILIUS
(9,315)

PLINUS
(10,500)

ROSS
(5,900)

CONDORCET
(10,100)

Hyginus Rille

BOSCOVICH
+15,400

JULIUS
CAESAR

TARUNTIUS
(2,950)

UKERT

TRIESNECKER
(9,515)

AGRIPPA
(9,800)

ARAGO
(5,900)

TRANQUILLITATIS
(SEA OF TRANQUILITY)

APOLLONIUS

MARE SPUMANS
(FOAMING SEA)

GODIN
(10,500)

RITTER   MARE

SABINE
(4,920)

1

MASKELYNE
(8,200)

EDII

3

DELAMBRE
(11,810)

2

MARE

HIPPARCHUS

TAYLOR   ALFRAGANUS

TORRICELLI
(6,890)

CARELLA
(10,660)

FECUNDITATIS
(SEA OF FERTILITY)

LANGRENUS

HALLEY

HIND

ISIDORUS
(9,940)

GUTENBERG
(7,480)

LA PÉROUSE

ALBATEGNIUS
+28,215

KLEIN
(11,435)

ABULFEDA
(10,500)

THEOPHILUS
(22,300)

MAGELHAENS
(6,430)

GOCLENIUS
(6,100)

MAGELHAENS-A

LOHSE

VOGEL
(7,870)

ARGELANDER
+13,845

CYRILLUS
(10,335)

MARE NECTARIS
(SEA OF NECTAR)

PYRENEES MTS.

COLOMBO–A

COLOMBO

VENDELINUS

ALMANON
(6,560)

BEAUMONT

COOK
(3,835)

GEBER
(9,610)

CATHARINA

MONGE
(8,465)

ABENEZRA
(10,500)

AZOPHI
(11,150)

ALTAI ESCARPMENT

FRACASTORIUS
(16,000)

SANTBECH
(13,100)

WROTTESLEY

PLAYFAIR

SACROBOSCO   20°

POLYBIUS
(7,740)

30°

FRACASTORIUS-B

40°   BORDA   50°   60°   70° 80°

PETAVIUS
(11,000)

WERNER
(10,170)

APIANUS
(10,170)

PONTANUS

Copyright by Rand McNally & Company

Lunar Landing Sites **1.** Sea of tranquility, 34°E, 2°40′N. **2.** Sea of Tranquility, 23°37′E, 0°45′N. **3.** Central Bay, 1°20′W, 0°25′N. **4.** Ocean of Storms, 36°25′W, 3°30′S. **5.** Ocean of Storms, 41°40′W, 1°40′N.

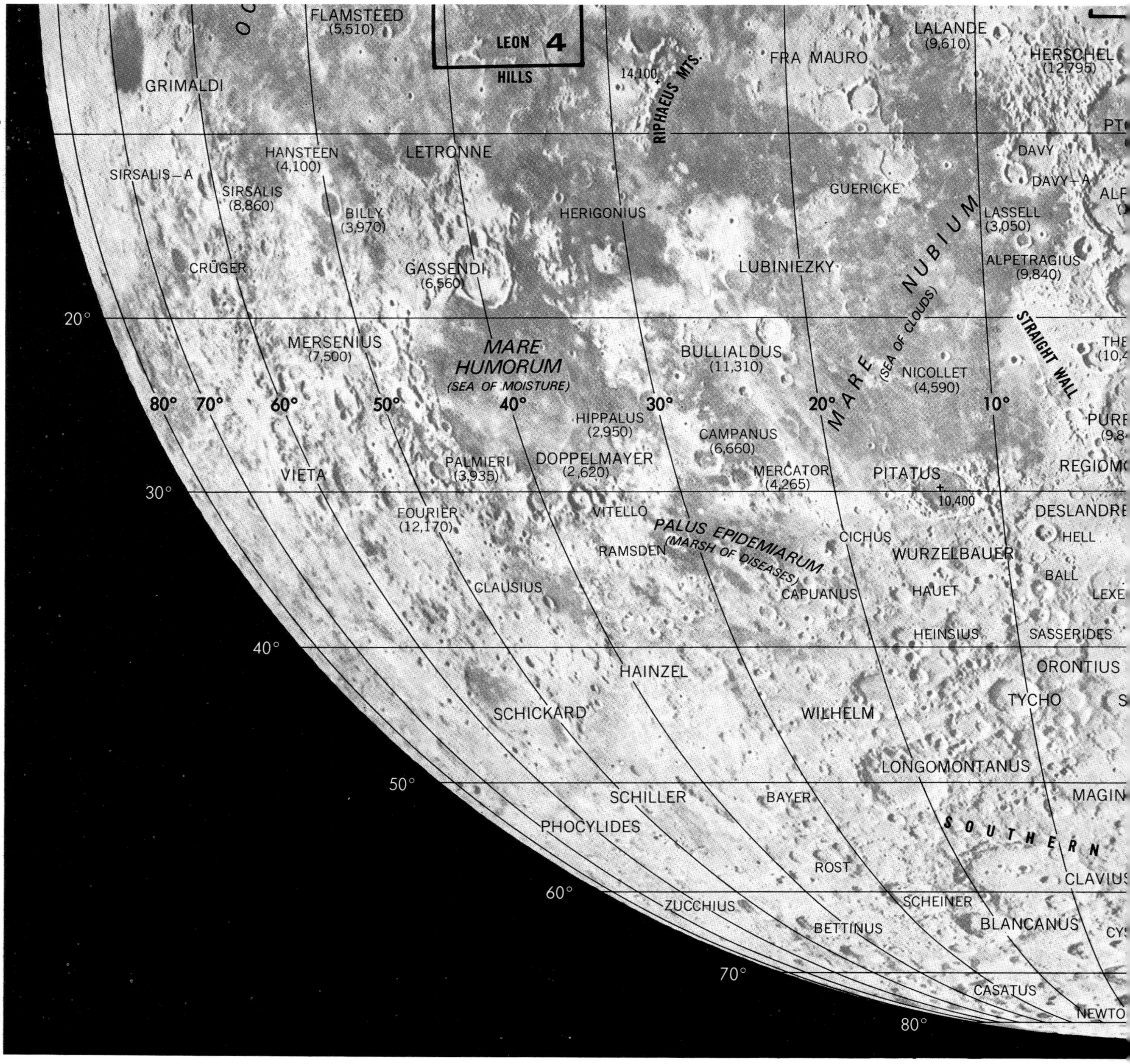

Map labels (Southern Area):

FLAMSTEED (5,510) · LEON 4 HILLS · 14,100 · RIPHAEUS MTS. · FRA MAURO · LALANDE (9,610) · HERSCHEL (12,795) · GRIMALDI · DAVY · DAVY–A · ALF · HANSTEEN (4,100) · LETRONNE · SIRSALIS–A · GUERICKE · SIRSALIS (8,860) · BILLY (3,970) · HERIGONIUS · LASSELL (3,050) · CRÜGER · GASSENDI (6,560) · LUBINIEZKY · ALPETRAGIUS (9,840) · MARE NUBIUM · MERSENIUS (7,500) · MARE HUMORUM (SEA OF MOISTURE) · BULLIALDUS (11,310) · STRAIGHT WALL · MARE (SEA OF CLOUDS) · NICOLLET (4,590) · THE (10,4) · 80° 70° 60° 50° 40° 30° 20° 10° · HIPPALUS (2,950) · CAMPANUS (6,660) · VIETA · PALMIERI (3,935) · DOPPELMAYER (2,620) · MERCATOR (4,265) · PITATUS · PURE (9,8) · FOURIER (12,170) · VITELLO · PALUS EPIDEMIARUM (MARSH OF DISEASES) · CICHUS · 10,400 · REGIOM · RAMSDEN · DESLANDRE · CLAUSIUS · CAPUANUS · WURZELBAUER · HELL · HAUET · BALL · LEXE · HEINSIUS · SASSERIDES · HAINZEL · ORONTIUS · SCHICKARD · WILHELM · TYCHO · S · LONGOMONTANUS · SOUTHERN · SCHILLER · BAYER · MAGIN · PHOCYLIDES · ROST · CLAVIUS · ZUCCHIUS · SCHEINER · BLANCANUS · CYS · BETTINUS · CASATUS · NEWTO

Latitude markings: 10° · 20° · 30° · 40° · 50° · 60° · 70° · 80°

ATLAS OF THE MOON

1 : 7600000

What to see: Southern Area

The southern uplands of the Moon are the roughest and most thickly cratered parts of the whole Earth-turned hemisphere. There are indeed so many craters that at first sight it is not easy to identify them. Pride of place must go to Clavius, not very far from the south polar area, which is 146 miles in diameter, and has high, massive walls; inside it are several craters of considerable size. Bailly, much closer to the Moon's limb, is larger than Clavius, but is never well seen from the Earth simply because it is so foreshortened. Tycho, a well-formed 54-mile crater, is the centre of a great system of bright rays, and dominates near Full Moon.

Schickard and Wargentin

Schickard, comparable in size with Clavius, has a darkish floor, and is always easy to find. Close by it is a most extraordinary formation, Wargentin, which appears to be filled with lava, so that its 'floor' is considerably elevated above the level of the outer surface; it is in fact in the nature of a plateau. It is not unique, since there are smaller formations of the same type, but no other plateau is nearly so large or so well preserved as the 56-mile Wargentin.

There are relatively few *mare* areas in this section, but it is worth noting the well-formed Mare Humorum (Sea of Humours), together with part of the Mare Nubium (Sea of Clouds). Over to the east there are large numbers of craters of all sizes, some of which (such as Petavius, with its central mountain and deep crack or cleft across the floor) are perfectly formed, while others (such

as Janssen) are in a ruinous condition. The Rheita Valley, or Vallis Rheita, was well shown on some of the Orbiter photographs, and proves to be a chain of craters rather than a true valley; a small telescope will show it well under suitable conditions of lighting. On the limb, some way from the Rheita Valley, is the Mare Australe or Southern Sea.

The Loftiest Peaks

The mountains near the Moon's south pole are very high, and some peaks in the Leibnitz range attain over 25,000 feet, but it must be remembered that these figures are somewhat arbitrary, because there is no convenient standard of reference such as sea-level on the Earth. The lunar mountains are comparable in height with the loftiest peaks on Earth—but since the Moon is a smaller globe, the mountains are much higher relatively.

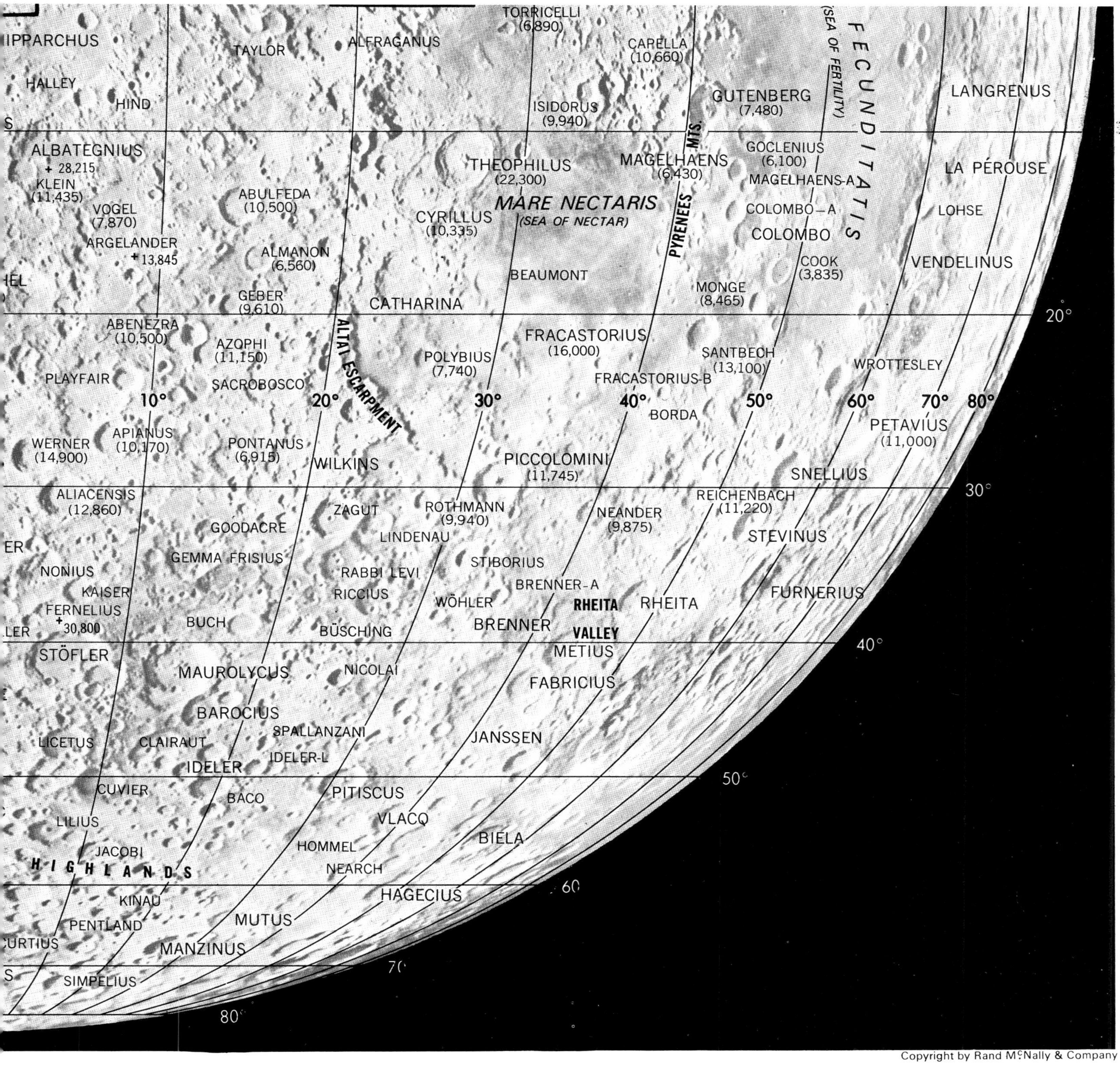

Map labels (Rand McNally lunar chart):

HIPPARCHUS · HALLEY · HIND · TAYLOR · ALFRAGANUS · TORRICELLI (6,890) · CARELLA (10,660) · FECUNDITATIS (SEA OF FERTILITY) · LANGRENUS
ALBATEGNIUS +28,215 · ISIDORUS (9,940) · GUTENBERG (7,480) · GOCLENIUS (6,100) · LA PÉROUSE
KLEIN (11,435) · THEOPHILUS (22,300) · MAGELHAENS (6,430) · MAGELHAENS-A · LOHSE
VOGEL (7,870) · ABULFEDA (10,500) · CYRILLUS (10,335) · MARE NECTARIS (SEA OF NECTAR) · COLOMBO-A · COLOMBO
ARGELANDER +13,845 · ALMANON (6,560) · COOK (3,835) · VENDELINUS
GEBER (9,610) · BEAUMONT · CATHARINA · MONGE (8,465)
ABENEZRA (10,500) · PYRENEES MTS · 20°
PLAYFAIR · AZOPHI (11,150) · POLYBIUS (7,740) · FRACASTORIUS (16,000) · SANTBECH (13,100) · WROTTESLEY
SACROBOSCO · ALTAI ESCARPMENT · FRACASTORIUS-B · BORDA
WERNER (14,900) · APIANUS (10,170) · PONTANUS (6,915) · WILKINS · PICCOLOMINI (11,745) · SNELLIUS · PETAVIUS (11,000)
ALIACENSIS (12,860) · GOODACRE · ZAGUT · ROTHMANN (9,940) · NEANDER (9,875) · REICHENBACH (11,220) · STEVINUS
NONIUS · GEMMA FRISIUS · LINDENAU · STIBORIUS · FURNERIUS
KAISER · RABBI LEVI · RICCIUS · WÖHLER · RHEITA · RHEITA VALLEY
FERNELIUS +30,800 · BUCH · BÜSCHING · BRENNER-A · BRENNER · METIUS
STÖFLER · MAUROLYCUS · NICOLAI · FABRICIUS
BAROCIUS · SPALLANZANI · JANSSEN
LICETUS · CLAIRAUT · IDELER · IDELER-L
CUVIER · BACO · PITISCUS · VLACQ · BIELA
LILIUS · HOMMEL · NEARCH
JACOBI · HIGHLANDS · HAGECIUS
KINAU · MUTUS
PENTLAND · MANZINUS
CURTIUS · SIMPELIUS

Copyright by Rand McNally & Company

THE FAR SIDE OF THE MOON

Until the flight of Lunik 3, the Russian probe of October 1959, the side of the Moon which is always turned away from the Earth remained very much of a mystery. Strange theories had been put forward from time to time; for instance, the nineteenth century Danish mathematician Hansen seriously suggested that all the lunar air and water had been drawn round to the far side, which might even be inhabited! However, most astronomers assumed that the hidden regions must be of the same type as those parts of the surface which we can see.

Attempts were made to locate ray-craters on the hidden hemisphere. As we have noted, there are some craters which are centres of bright ray systems; the best examples on the Earth-turned hemisphere are Copernicus and Tycho. Observers tracked down some faint rays coming across the limb from the far side of the Moon, and did their best to estimate the positions of the unknown craters responsible for them. Yet nothing much could be done until the launching of suitable probes—and this took place with Lunik 3, sent up by the Russians exactly two years after the ascent of their first artificial satellite, Sputnik 1.

Lunik 3

Lunik 3 went on a round-the-Moon flight. While over the hidden side, it took photographs, and these photographs were later transmitted to the Earth. One of them is shown below. It includes part of the familiar face as well as the far side, and the well-formed Mare Crisium is easy to recognize. To the right of this region there are some definite features, notably the darkish plain which the Russians named the Sea of Moscow. The blackish spot lower down in the picture is called Tsiolkovskii, in honour of the great rocket pioneer, and is now known to be a crater; the photograph of it taken much later, during the U.S. Orbiter programme, shows it excellently.

The early Lunik 3 pictures seem blurred by modern standards, and there was only one 'active pass' beyond the Moon; signals from the probe ceased abruptly after the photograph transmission, and contact was never re-established. Neither were the pictures easy to interpret; for instance, the first maps from them showed what seemed to be a chain of peaks (the Soviet Mountains) which are now known not to exist at all. Yet the achievement was great, and the photographs proved that the only real difference between the two hemispheres is that the Earth-turned side contains more of the grey maria.

The Orbiters

For some years after their triumph with Lunik III the Russians sent up no more successful probes to the Moon, and the next major development came with the American Orbiter programme, between 1966 and 1968. Vehicles were put into circum-lunar orbits, and extensive photography was carried out. By the time that the Orbiter programme was over, almost all of the Moon—including the far side—had been studied in great detail. The limited areas not covered by the Orbiters had been photographed by another Russian probe, Zond 3, though it must be admitted that the quality of the Zond pictures was not nearly so good as those from the Orbiters.

The relative lack of maria on the far side was confirmed. On the other hand, there were some formations of exceptional interest, notably the Mare Orientale (Eastern Sea), which can just be seen from Earth when it is brought into view by favourable conditions of libration. It had been thought that the Mare Orientale must be an ordinary dark plain of the same general type as the Mare Crisium, but the Orbiter photographs showed it to be more extensive than had been anticipated. Arguments about its origin were still going on when the first men went round the Moon. Some astronomers regarded the Mare Orientale as a complex volcanic structure, while others considered it to be due to the impact of a meteorite.

The presence of ray-craters on the far side of the Moon was confirmed, and it was found that the earlier estimates, made by studying the rays coming across the limb on to the Earth-turned side, were not greatly in error. There were also various large crater-valleys of the same type as the famous Rheita Valley. Also, there were large enclosures which might have looked like maria but for the fact that their floors were light in hue instead of dark. On the whole, however, the aspect was one of a very thickly-cratered surface.

The reason for the scarcity of maria on the Moon's far side is not known, but it is reasonable to suppose that the gravitational force of the Earth must be involved; it is very likely that the lunar rotation has been captured (i.e. equal to its period of revolution) since an early stage in the history of the Earth-Moon system.

The Mascons

Another important point follows from the lack of maria. Studies of the movements of circum-lunar probes, mainly the Orbiters, had shown that underneath some of the familiar seas, such as the Mare Imbrium and the Mare Serenitatis, there were dense regions which exerted enough pull to disturb the movements of the probes. These regions were called mascons, from *mass concentrations*. There were suggestions that they might be buried iron meteorites; alternatively, and perhaps more logically, it was proposed that a mascon might not be a definite body, but simply a sub-crustal area where the rock density was unusually high. In either case, it seemed safe to assume that there would be no mascons on the far side, simply because there were no large circular seas.

Conditions on the Far Side

It must always be remembered that so far as the Sun is concerned, day and night conditions on the Moon's hidden side are exactly the same as on the Earth-turned hemisphere—but the nights will be darker, since the Earth can never been seen. Moreover, once a probe passes behind the Moon as seen from the Earth, its signals are cut off. This happened to Apollo 8 and Apollo 10—and in each case the vital engine-firing designed to put the probe into a path round the Moon had to be carried out during this period of isolation. And the impossibility of calling up the Earth direct from the hidden side will certainly preclude the establishment of manned bases there—at least until a chain of communications satellites is set up round the Moon.

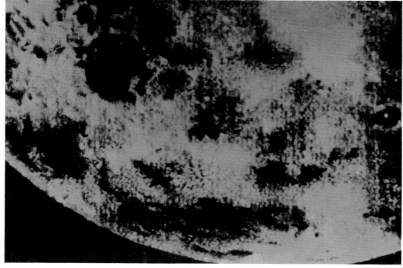

First Far-side Photograph
The first photograph of the Moon's far side was taken by the Soviet vehicle Lunik 3 (or Luna 3) in October 1959. Lacking in detail though it may be, compared with later photographs, this was an historic picture. The Mare Crisium, which is of course visible from the Earth, is shown unmistakably, but most of the areas lie on the averted hemisphere. Note, in particular, the dark-floored crater Tsiolkovskii, with its bright central peak.

Tsiolkovskii
Orbiter 3, launched in February 1967, was one of the most successful probes in the whole series. Among the photographs obtained was a spectacular view of the crater Tsiolkovskii, on the Moon's far side. It is interesting to compare this photograph with the pioneer picture of the same formation obtained by Russia's Lunik 3 almost eight years before. Tsiolkovskii is noted for the darkness of parts of its floor.

MARE SMYTHII

MARE AUSTRALE

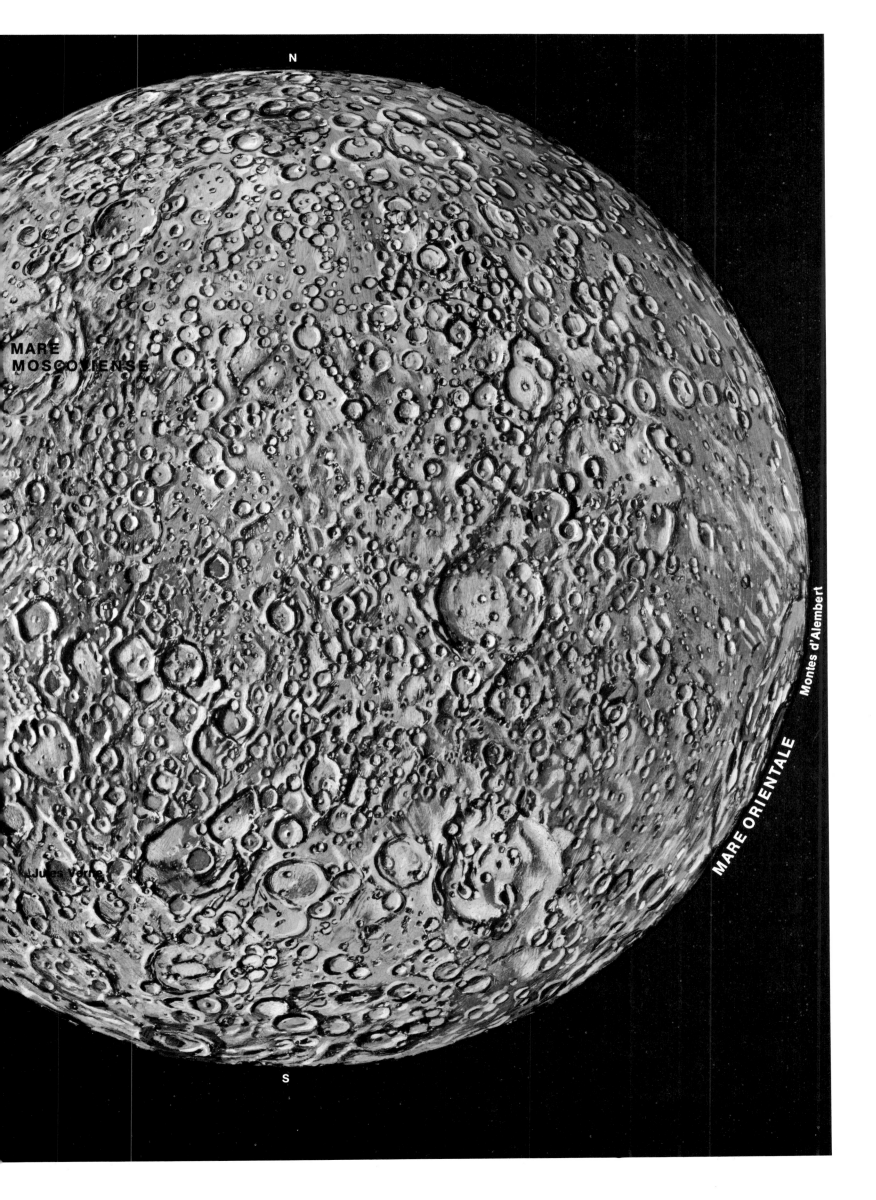

N

MARE
MOSCOVIENSE

Jules Verne

Montes d'Alembert

MARE ORIENTALE

N

S

THE APOLLO PLAN

1 Pre-launch. The Saturn rocket on its launching-pad stands over 360 feet in height. There are five clustered engines on the 138-foot first stage; these burn 470 tons of propellant in 2 minutes 10 seconds, and raise the speed to 6,000 m.p.h. The launching is suitably spectacular!

2 The launching must, of course, be according to the "step" principle. The first separation comes soon after blast-off; the lower stage, its work done, falls back to the ground. This part of the manœuvre too is spectacular—and probably looks more alarming to watchers from Earth than it seems to the astronauts themselves!

3 The second stage separates. The single engine of the third stage fires for 2 minutes; the vehicle is now at a height of 115 miles. Then the engine of the third stage fires again, and raises the velocity to over 24,000 m.p.h. This sends the vehicle into an orbit which will take it to the Moon.

4 The next manœuvre is the separatio of the L.E.M., or Lunar Excursion Mod L.E.M. could not return to Earth; it i designed entirely for the lunar landi Here the Command Module separate from the launching position with th L.E.M. to re-dock for the flight posi

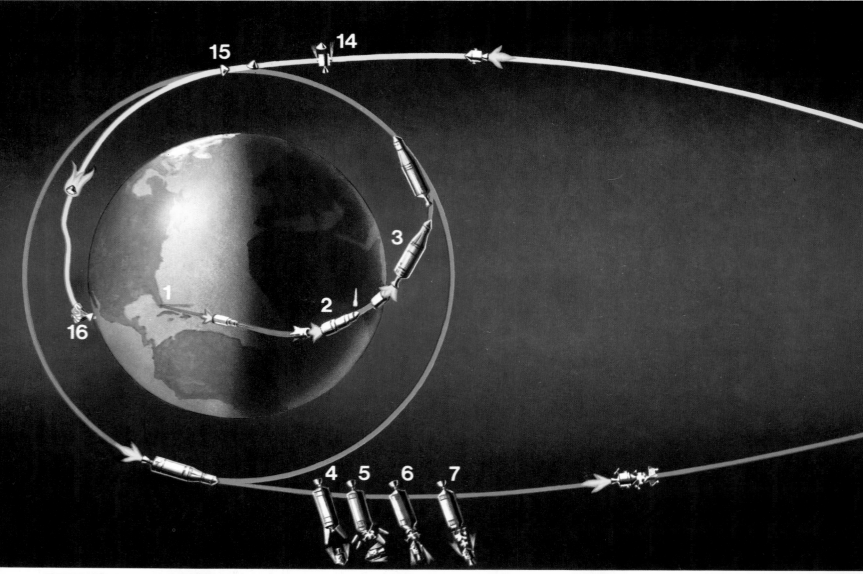

9 The L.E.M. moves away from the Command Module, and fires its engines. This will take the Module out of lunar orbit, and it will begin its descent toward the Moon. As soon as this has been done, the two astronauts in the L.E.M. are very much 'on their own', since the Command Module could not make a lunar landing.

10 Landing on the Moon. The engines of the L.E.M. slow it down until it is immediately above the surface, and the final touch-down is gentle. A certain amount of manœuvra-bility is possible, but only within rather restricted limits, so that this is one of the most hazardous moments of the entire expedition.

11 After the service investigations are over, the engines of the L.E.M. are again fired, so that the module can return to rendezvous with the waiting Command Module. The bottom part of the L.E.M. acts as a launching pad, and is left behind on the Moon.

12 Rendezvous with the Command Module which has been circling the Moon whil astronauts in the L.E.M. have been on t surface. Radio contact has been mainta Docking is carried out, and the two astronauts of the L.E.M. re-enter the Command Module ready for the return t Earth.

5 The Command Module now turns on its axis to dock with the L.E.M. to make the complete lunar craft for the flight to the Moon. The Command Module will remain in orbit round the Moon while the L.E.M. descends to the surface.

6 The lunar craft is separated from the third stage; the vehicle is now correctly assembled for the final journey to the Moon. Launching could not have been carried out in this way, as the astronauts had then to be in the top of the vehicle.

7 The separation is completed. The third stage of the launcher is jettisoned, as its work too is done, and the astronauts are left in the actual Moon vehicle. Relatively little now remains of the immense structure which was originally assembled on the launching pad at Cape Kennedy.

8 After the 239,000 mile flight from Earth the Command Module fires its rockets to brake the lunar craft 80 miles above the Moon's surface. This sends the craft into a pre-calculated orbit round the Moon. Now the lunar-landing crew crawl through the docking hatch from the Command Module to the L.E.M.

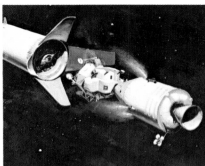

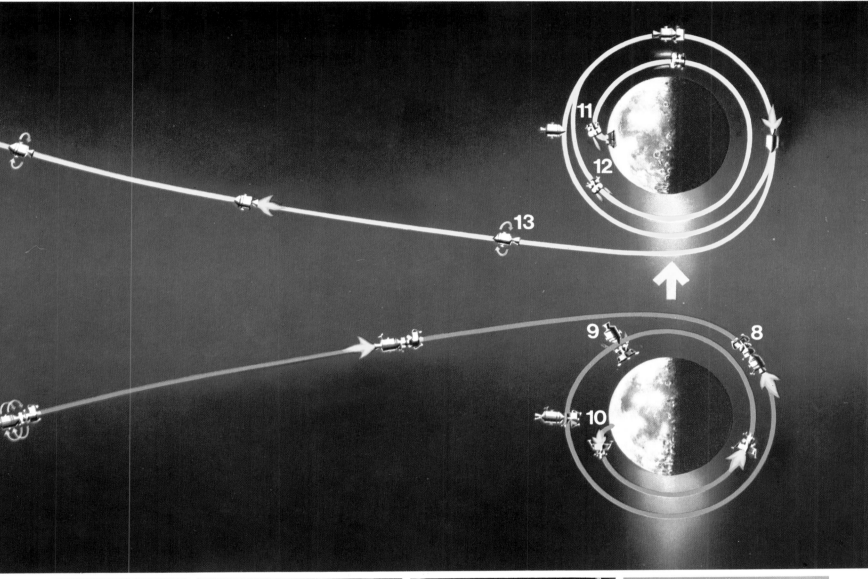

13 Before firing the engines of the Command Module for the homeward journey, the top stage of the L.E.M. is jettisoned, and is fired off into space; its work is done, and it cannot be recovered. It must be separated so that there is no danger of subsequent collision with it.

14 Just before the vehicle enters the Earth's atmosphere, the Service Module section is jettisoned, leaving only the Command Module—a small craft 13 feet in diameter at the blunt end. The Service Module does not return to the ground, but is put into orbit.

15 Reaction control jets are fired, turning the Command Module so that its heat-shield points toward the Earth. The temperature on the heat-shield will inevitably rise to at least 5000 degrees Centigrade, and it is essential for the re-entry angle to be correct.

16 Drogue parachutes are used, followed by the main parachutes which bring the Command Module down gently into the sea. The final landing is made at a speed of less than 25 m.p.h. Rescue ships are waiting for the returned astronauts; the long journey to the Moon and back is over.

23

MEN IN SPACE

(left) **The Apollo 7 Launch**

The Astronauts

It is one thing to develop a vehicle which can send men to the Moon; it is quite another to select and train the men who are to make the journey. An astronaut has to have both ability and stability. He must be physically fit, so that he can cope with the immense stress of a space-voyage; he must be familiar with every detail of his vehicle; he must be able to make scientific observations of all kinds, and he must be ready for any emergency. Moreover, he must be able to work in perfect harmony with his companions.

Few people could meet all these requirements, and it is no coincidence that all the early astronauts (and Russian cosmonauts) were also test pilots. The training, too, is remarkably rigorous. There are physical and psychological tests; the astronaut must be so well prepared that nothing is left to chance. It takes several years to make an astronaut ready for his first voyage beyond the Earth.

The initial blast-off means that the astronauts are subjected to considerable pressure. Also, it is notable that it takes a very large vehicle to send a very small module to the Moon. Fully assembled, the Saturn rocket on its launching pad stands over 360 feet in height, but the L.E.M. or Lunar Excursion Module, is a mere 22 feet 11 inches high and 31 feet wide. The L.E.M. itself, of course, never returns to the Earth, and would be incapable of doing so. All that comes back is the cone-shaped capsule containing the three astronauts. The rest of the huge structure on the launching-pad is expendable—and this is one reason why lunar voyages are so expensive; the vehicle can be used only once. In the future, atomic motors will no doubt be developed, and this will mean that there will be no need to use the cumbersome 'step-method' which is so wasteful; but adequate atomic motors are not in sight as yet.

The Space-Suit

Another essential piece of equipment is the space-suit. The design actually in use today is very different from the rigid suit described in so many science-fiction novels. It is comparatively flexible, and is not so uncomfortable as might be expected, but it has to have many special features, and it must be foolproof. The Moon has to all intents and purposes no atmosphere, so that a lunar suit and a 'deep-space' suit are identical—and any astronaut who is standing on the Moon's surface will have to be on his guard; he depends entirely upon his suit. To describe one of many features, there is the question of the disposal of body waste. Urine is collected in a container attached to the inside of the suit; more solid waste is dealt with by absorbent material. Needless to say, the oxygen supply is of

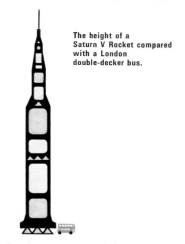

The height of a Saturn V Rocket compared with a London double-decker bus.

prime importance, and there are special cooling devices in the under-suit—without which the astronaut would become dangerously overheated when carrying out any tasks involving physical exertion.

One of the most important tasks of the Apollo mission is to find out more about the Moon itself. Samples of the lunar crust are collected, and brought back for analysis. Though the Moon is almost certainly sterile, and has never known life, stringent precautions must be taken; there is always the chance, however remote, that harmful contamination will be brought back to the Earth, in which case it might spread with alarming rapidity. (The danger is very real in the case of Mars, which has an appreciable atmosphere, and may well support some form of primitive life.) The lunar samples are 'quarantined' until the scientific teams are satisfied that no risk of contamination remains. Only then are the samples brought out and distributed to research workers.

Sampling Equipment

The samples are collected by means of special tools, which are really in the

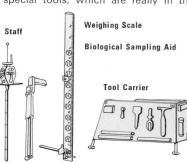

Staff · Weighing Scale · Biological Sampling Aid · Tool Carrier

---

Rocket Development

1902

Tsiolkovskii—In 1902 Konstantin Eduardovich Tsiolkovskii, a shy, deaf Russian school-teacher, published the first of his papers dealing with rocketry and space-flight. His work attracted no attention at the time, but a surprising number of his theories proved to be correct, and he is justly regarded as 'the father of space-flight'.
(below)
Tsiolkovskii and one of his designs.

1926

Goddard—Tsiolkovskii was purely a theorist, and the greatest of the early practical rocket experimenters was Robert Goddard, who began his research in the first decade of the 20th century—quite independently of Tsiolkovskii. In 1926 he fired the first liquid-fuel rocket. It was primitive and feeble, but it was successful. *(right)* Goddard's Rocket Launcher.

1949

The First Step-Rocket—During the war, high-altitude rockets were developed by the German team led by Wernher von Braun. After 1945, captured rockets were taken to America. In 1949 a WAC Corporal rocket was mounted on top of a German vehicle, and sent up to 244 miles—a record at that time. This was the first time that the step-rocket principle had been used.

1957

Sputnik 1—In 1955 the Americans announced that they meant to launch an artificial satellite during the International Geophysical Year of 1957-8. However, the first orbital vehicle was Russian, Sputnik 1, launched on October 4, 1957. It remained aloft until January 1958, and sent back radio signals. Tiny by modern standards, it marked the beginning of the Space Age. *(below)* Sputnik 1.

1961

First Man in Space—The first man in space was also a Russian. On April 12, Major (later Colonel) Yuri Gagarin was launched in Vostok 1, and made a complete circuit of the Earth, landing safely near the pre-arranged position. It is tragic that Gargarin did not live to see the full results of his pioneer flight, he was killed in an aircraft crash in 1967. *(below)* Vostok 1.

nature of 'core-samplers of the type used by geologists. Storage cases are, of course, included in the astronauts' equipment. Another interesting experiment is to leave seismological instruments on the lunar surface. We do not yet know whether there are any minor ground tremors which may be called 'moonquakes'; if there are, the seismological equipment will detect them and send back information. As the Apollo programme goes on, more and more equipment will be left on the Moon.

All this is a preliminary to the setting-up of full-scale lunar bases. As yet the design of these bases is very much a matter of opinion. The attractive, dome-like structures, made of plastic and kept inflated by the pressure of air inside them, may or may not prove to be practicable, and it is quite likely that lunar stations will have to be constructed underground, either by making caves or by utilizing natural ones. Clearly, it is desirable to establish a proper base as soon as possible, so that an adequately-equipped scientific laboratory can be brought into operation.

The Return to Earth

There remains the question of the return to Earth, and the final landing. With the Apollo programme, the astronauts splash down in the ocean, following their re-entry into the air and the release of parachutes. This means that ships must be ready in the splashdown area, so that the astronauts can be picked up—and incidentally, to make sure that the capsule floats. (On one occasion, in the Mercury programme, a capsule actually sank, and the astronaut narrowly escaped drowning.) By now, the landing procedure has become so accurate that the capsule is brought down within sight of the waiting rescue ships.

The Russian procedure has been somewhat different, inasmuch as the landings have been made on land instead of in the sea. No doubt this will also be adopted by the Americans eventually, but at the moment the ocean splashdown is regarded as safer, and has proved to be quite satisfactory.

Sample Return Containers

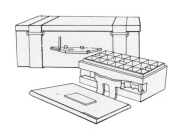

Extra-vehicular suit
The outer layer is of Teflon-coated yarn and Beta glass-fibre fabric, which is completely non-inflammable in an oxygen atmosphere. Beneath this are another seven layers of synthetic materials which serve as insulators and liners.

VHF antenna linked to space craft

Oxygen purge system
Provides an emergency 30-minute supply of oxygen in two 2-lb bottles.

Backpack
Supplies oxygen and cooling water to the liquid cooling garment; return oxygen is cleansed. The pack also includes communications equipment, controls and a main power supply.

Oxygen purge system umbilical

Lunar Module restraint ring

Gloves
Made of Chromel-R fabric and with thermal insulation for protection against extremes of heat and cold.

Urine transfer connector

Extravehicular visor
A polycarbonate shell placed over the helmet. It is thermally controlled, coated with gold to reduce light and heat from the sun, and is of high impact strength.

Backpack control

Penlight pocket

Utility pocket

Lunar overshoes

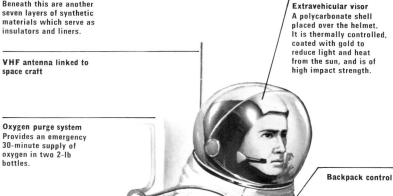
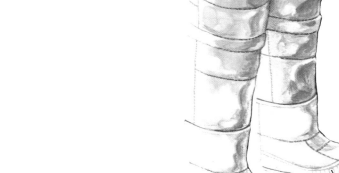

Liquid cooling garment
A knitted nylon-spandex garment worn next to the skin, with a network of plastic tubing through which cooling water from the portable life support system is circulated.

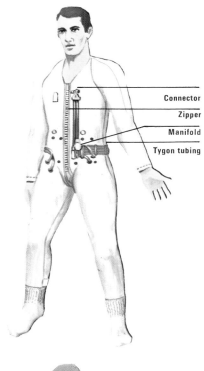

Connector

Zipper

Manifold

Tygon tubing

Diagram of the Tygon tubing carrying the liquid cooling system.

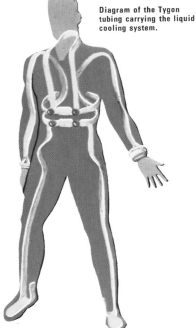

1961
First American Sub-Orbital Flight— When Gagarin made his ascent in Vostok 1, the Americans were still not ready to begin their manned space programme, but on May 5, 1961, Commander Alan Shepard made a sub-orbital flight to a height of 116 miles. It was more or less of an 'up and down' trip, and was of short duration, but it was entirely successful, and Shepard has the honour of being the first American to enter space.

1962
Project Mercury — The Mercury project involved space-orbits by single astronauts. Following Shepard's sub-orbital flight, and a second similar trip by the late Virgil Grissom, Colonel John Glenn achieved a complete orbit, like Gagarin. This was the first of several similar trips, though Glenn himself did not make another space-flight. *(right)* Mercury Capsule.

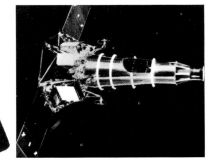

1964
The Ranger Programme— Project Mercury was followed by the Gemini launchings, involving two astronauts in one capsule, and complicated manoeuvres such as 'space-walks'. Meanwhile, probes were being sent to the Moon. The Ranger vehicles were crash-landed on the Moon; during the last few minutes of their flights, they sent back close-range pictures of the lunar surface. The first six failed, but the last three were successful. *(below)* Ranger vehicle.

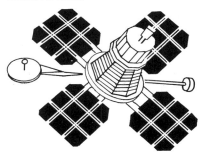

1966
The Orbiters— The Russians were the first to put a vehicle into orbit round the Moon, but particularly good results were obtained from the U.S. Orbiters, which were placed in lunar orbit and which sent back many thousands of detailed photographs of almost the entire surface— including the side of the Moon which is always turned away from the Earth. The information obtained from the Orbiters was an essential preliminary to the Apollo programme. *(below)* An Orbiter.

1966-8
Soft Landings on The Moon— Once again the Russians took the lead in bringing a vehicle down gently on the Moon, so that pictures could be sent back from the lunar surface; this was first done with Luna 9 in 1966. Subsequently, more soft landings were made both by Russian Luna probes and by the U.S. Surveyors. The photographs obtained were invaluable. *(below)* A detail of the lunar surface showing a landing pad from a Surveyor.

THE LUNAR MODULE

Launch Escape System
This propels the Command Module to safety in the event of an aborted launch

Command Module
11 feet 5 inches high: contains reaction control engines and crew compartment.

Service Module
24 feet 7 inches high: contains propulsion systems, fuel cells, oxygen, hydrogen and food for the crew.

Lunar Module
Two-stage vehicle, 22 feet 11 inches high.

Instrument Unit
3 feet high, this contains guidance, navigation and control equipment for Earth orbits and injection into lunar orbit.

Third Stage
58 feet high, this has one J-2 engine burning liquid oxygen and liquid hydrogen. This fires twice: the first burn places the spacecraft into Earth orbit; the second sends the vehicle into an orbit which will take it to the Moon at 24,000 m.p.h.

Second Stage
81.5 feet high, this stage has five J-2 engines burning liquid oxygen and liquid hydrogen. It fires for 6 minutes and lifts the vehicle almost to Earth orbit (101.6 nautical miles) at 14,000 m.p.h.

First Stage
138 feet high this stage has five F-1 engines burning liquid oxygen. It boosts the vehicle to 6,000 m.p.h. and to an altitude of 35.8 nautical miles After 2 minutes 40 seconds it is separated, falling into the Atlantic.

SATURN V LAUNCH VEHICLE (281 feet)

SPACECRAFT (82 feet)

Saturn V

The Saturn V, 363 feet tall with the Apollo spacecraft in place, would be capable of sending about 50 tons of payload into lunar orbit. The first stage fires its motors for 2 minutes 40 seconds, taking the vehicle up to a height of just over 40 miles and a speed of over 6,000 m.p.h. It then separates, and falls back into the Atlantic Ocean. The second stage, 82 feet in height and 33 feet in diameter, has five engines, and carries the rocket to a altitude of over 115 miles before it too separates and falls back into the sea. The third stage, with a height of 58·3 feet, has one engine, using liquid oxygen and liquid hydrogen as propel-

The Lunar Module

The Lunar Module is very different from the sleek, streamlined Moonships so often described in the past. There is, in fact, no need to streamline it at all, because it is not intended for operation in atmosphere. Its sole function is to take two Apollo astronauts down from the Command Module to the surface of the Moon and back again. Also, its construction appears superficially rather flimsy—since it operates only in space and under conditions of the relatively

containing the guidance, navigation and control equipment which steers the vehicle through its Earth orbits and into the final path toward the Moon.

hatches are secured, both the probe and drogue assemblies are removed from the vehicle tunnels, to allow free crew transfer between the two Modules.

The Lunar Module itself is a two-stage vehicle, but the two parts operate as a single unit until the final blast-off from the Moon. At this point the lower stage is used as a launching pad, and only the upper part returns to orbit to rendezvous with the Command Module which has remained in orbit.

The Lunar Module is by no means so roomy as the Command Module. What may be termed its 'habitable volume' is only 160 cubic feet, so that for a long space-voyage it would be decidedly cramped—but in the Apollo programme

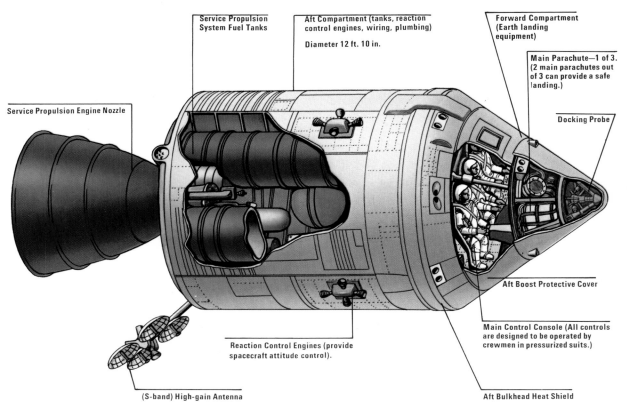

Service Propulsion System Fuel Tanks

Aft Compartment (tanks, reaction control engines, wiring, plumbing)

Diameter 12 ft. 10 in.

Forward Compartment (Earth landing equipment)

Main Parachute—1 of 3. (2 main parachutes out of 3 can provide a safe landing.)

Service Propulsion Engine Nozzle

Docking Probe

Aft Boost Protective Cover

Main Control Console (All controls are designed to be operated by crewmen in pressurized suits.)

Reaction Control Engines (provide spacecraft attitude control).

(S-band) High-gain Antenna

Aft Bulkhead Heat Shield

lants. This engine comes into action immediately after the separation of the second stage, and operates for 156 seconds, putting the space-craft into an orbit round the Earth. Over 2½ hours later the engine is again operated, and the space-craft is put into an orbit which will take it to the Moon.

The Instrument Unit

The instrument unit is a cylinder 3 feet high and 21 feet 8 inches in diameter, weighing over 4,000 pounds, and

weak gravity of the Moon.

When lunar orbit has been achieved, the Lunar Module or L.E.M. (Lunar Excursion Module) is made ready for the descent. Both it and the Command Module are equipped with what is known as 'probe-and-drogue docking hardware'. The probe assembly is a folding coupling and impact-attenuating device mounted on the Command Module tunnel, mating with a conical drogue mounted on the Lunar Module docking tunnel. After the docking

it is in use for only a relatively short time, and of course it has to carry only two astronauts instead of three. The cylindrical crew compartment is made of fusion-welded aluminium sheet, and is 92 inches in diameter by 42 inches deep. There are two triangular front windows and a 32-inch square inward-opening forward hatch in the front face.

Landing Manœuvres

One very important feature of the design concerns the four foot-pads.

Crew Transfer
Before the descent to the Moon begins, the two astronauts who are to go down must leave the Command Module and enter the Lunar Module through the 'tunnel', as is shown in the diagram below. After the lunar flight, the two vehicles are docked, and once again the astronauts pass through the tunnel — this time back into the Command Module.

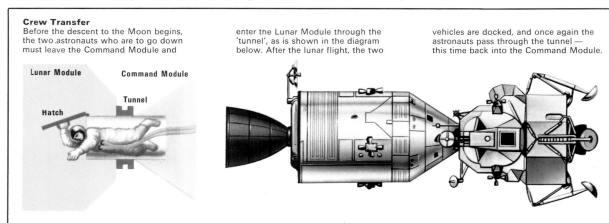

Lunar Module   Command Module

Hatch   Tunnel

Though there is a certain amount of room for manœuvre when the Module is about to make its landing on the Moon, there is always the chance of coming down on an uneven area, and—as has been noted—a sharp tilt would cause a highly dangerous situation. The Module must be able to right 'itself' as much as possible, so that the bottom stage is left in a position suitable for it to be used as a launching pad when the time comes to leave the Moon.

Testing the Lunar Module

During the early stages of the Apollo programme, it was widely supposed that the Lunar Module might prove to be the weak link in the programme. Testing it was difficult, inasmuch as it was not designed to operate in the Earth's atmosphere—and one early attempt ended in an undignified crash, fortunately without causing any casualty. It was for this purpose that Apollo 9 was launched in 1969. Unlike Apollo 8, this mission was not a Moonshot, and Apollo 9 remained in an orbit round the Earth. Separation of the Lunar Module was carried out, and Astronauts Schweickart and McDivett flew it successfully; at one time they were over 100 miles from Astronaut Scott, who remained in the Command Module. It was the success of this manœuvre which paved the way for the 'lunar swoop' of Astronauts Stafford and Cernan in Apollo 10, in May 1969, and for the lunar landing with Apollo 11.

Small though it may be, the Lunar Module is an extremely complex vehicle, since it has to have all the life-supporting equipment of the Command Module itself. Strange though it may look, it has proved its worth and its reliability—even though 'Snoopy', the nickname given to the Lunar Module of Apollo 10, did give a certain amount of trouble, both during the rendezvous manœuvre and when it subsequently appeared dangerously close to the Command Module ('Charlie Brown') after it had been finally jettisoned and its two astronauts had rejoined Commander Young in the main craft!

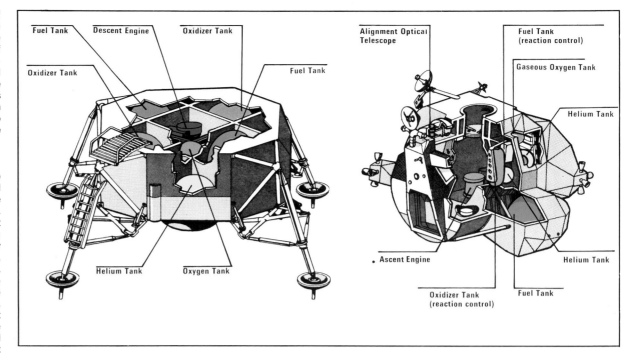

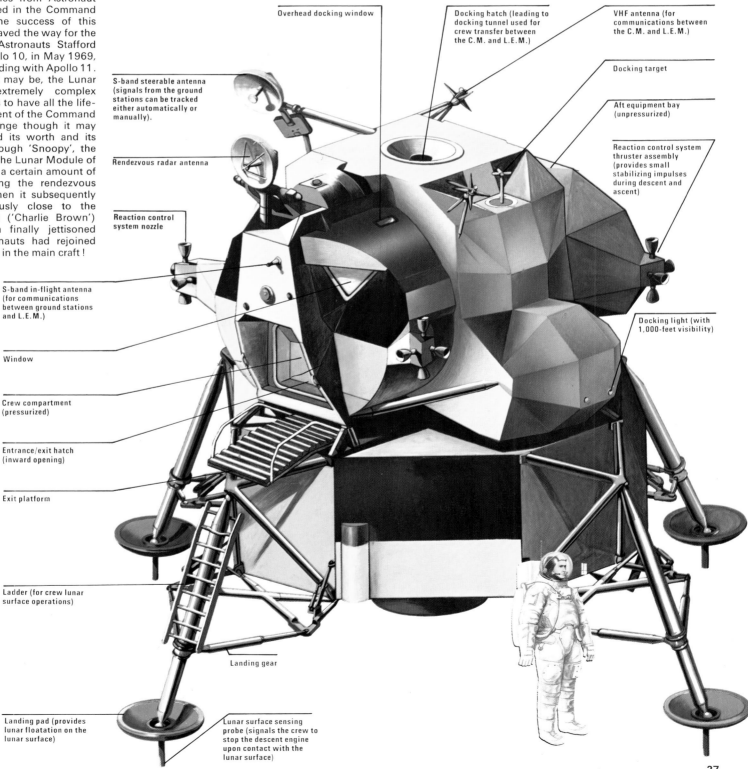

27

APOLLO 8

Manned exploration of the Moon began on December 21, 1968, with the launching of Apollo 8. Aboard were three astronauts, Frank Borman, James Lovell and William Anders; their mission was to put their spaceship into a path round the Moon, and study the lunar scene from a height of less than 70 miles.

It is history now that the flight was completely successful, and to all intents and purposes trouble-free, but it was also extremely dangerous, inasmuch as the astronauts were carrying out manœuvres which had never· been attempted before. No man had ever been more than a few hundreds of miles from the Earth; Apollo 8 was destined to travel a quarter of a million.

Messages were received regularly during the outward flight, and by December 24 Apollo 8 was nearing the Moon. Then it went behind the Moon as seen from Earth, and communication was cut off; this was the first loss of signal or LOS. While out of touch, the astronauts fired their motors, and put themselves into a circum-lunar orbit. Only when they 'came out' from behind the Moon, and sent back their first radio message, did the controllers at Houston Base know that all was well.

Travelling round the Moon at about 3,700 m.p.h., Apollo 8 completed ten circuits. Contact was maintained except during the LOS periods, and the astronauts took large numbers of photographs. The next manœuvre was another engine firing to break free from lunar orbit; this too was accomplished faultlessly, and at 15/51 hours G.M.T. on December 27 the astronauts splashed down in the South Pacific very close to the position where the rescue ships were waiting for them.

Had Apollo 8 failed for any reason, the American space programme would have been delayed for a long time. The fact that it did not fail is a tribute both to the designers and planners, who left nothing to chance, and to the skill and courage of the three members of the crew, who did everything that could have been expected of them. Apollo 8 did indeed mark the beginning of a new era in space research.

Apollo 8 was essentially a flight to test the reliability of the probe itself, and photography of the Moon was a secondary consideration. Nevertheless, Astronauts Borman, Lovell and Anders came back with some excellent photographs of the Moon and of the Earth seen from almost a quarter of a million miles.

The Approaching Moon

During their flight, only part of the Moon's Earth-turned hemisphere was illuminated. The Mare Crisium was in sunlight; so were the interesting areas of the Mare Fœcunditatis and the Mare Tranquillitatis. It followed, of course, that part of the hemisphere turned away from the Earth was also having its period of day. This is shown on the photograph, in which the Mare Crisium can be recognized to the left of the centre of the Moon's disk. The areas above and to the right of the Mare Crisium cannot be seen from Earth; note the dark-floored crater Tsiolkovskii, which is prominent close to the edge of the disk to the upper right. Even the central peak of the crater can be made out easily.

Even more spectacular was the photograph of the Earth in the lunar sky, taken by Colonel Borman on Christmas Eve during their period in orbit round the Moon. In his own words, sent back during a message to the rocket base in Houston: 'There's a beautiful earth out here'—and the photograph bears this out. It is not easy to make out the continents and the oceans, because of the presence of clouds which veil large areas of the surface, but the overall sight was magnificent. Because the Moon has no atmosphere, the lunar sky is always black, but the astronauts reported that it was difficult to see stars from the space-craft when Apollo 8 was above the sunlit side of the Moon. When the craft was over the dark side, or in translunar space (that is, the space region between the Earth and the Moon), the stars could be seen in all their glory.

Round the Moon

During its ten circuits of the Moon, Apollo 8 passed over some of the familiar features of the eastern hemisphere. In particular there was the grand crater Langrenus, well over 100 miles in diameter, with its massive, terraced walls and its central peaks. Langrenus lies on the edge of the Mare Fœcunditatis, and is one of the most imposing features of the Moon; but nobody before the Apollo 8 astronauts had seen it in such detail. When Colonel Borman took the photograph (below right), the space-ship was only about 70 miles above the Moon.

Features of the hidden side were also photographed, and many craters were recorded, some of which were the centres of ray-systems. The astronauts confirmed that the hemisphere turned away from the Earth is relatively rough (even by lunar standards!) and they also confirmed that there was no marked local colour. They reported that from their space-craft they could actually see more detail than is shown in the photographs.

When Apollo 8 splashed down after its pioneer voyage, few people doubted that the first landing on the Moon would become possible in the near future. Astronauts Borman, Lovell and Anders had taken their honoured place in the history of space research.

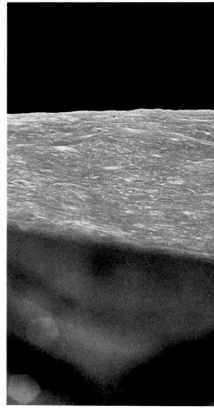

The Moon (left)
The Moon, seen from translunar space by the astronauts of Apollo 8. The well-formed Mare Crisium (Maps: 14 and 20) is seen to the top of the picture; the Mare Fœcunditatis (Map: 19) is below the centre of the photograph. The dark feature near the limb, on the lower right, is the crater Tsiolkovskii, which is on the far side of the Moon and can never be seen from Earth.

The Earth in the lunar sky (below)
This photograph was taken by Colonel Borman as Apollo 8 travelled round the Moon; it was not, strictly speaking, on the 'schedule' for photographs, but is certainly one of the most spectacular pictures obtained during the entire flight.

Lunar Craters as photographed by the Astronauts of Apollo 8
The largest crater shown is Goclenius (Map 26), which is 32 miles in diameter, and whose walls rise to 5,000 feet above the deepest part of the sunken floor. The system of cracks or clefts on the interior is very striking. The photograph was taken on December 25, while Apollo 8 was circling the Moon.

Crater on the far side of the Moon
Photographed from Apollo 8 on December 25, 1968. The area covered in the picture is 50 miles square, at lunar latitude 4° 5′ S., longitude 157 W. The main crater is 20 miles in diameter, and actually lies on the floor of a much larger crater.

Lunar craters (above right)
The craters were photographed during the time when Apollo 8 was in a closed orbit round the Moon on Christmas Day, 1968. The details shown are very complex, and Colonel Borman summed up the general aspect in one word: 'Desolation'—a term which could hardly be bettered.

Langrenus (below right)
The huge crater Langrenus (Map : 26) with its high terraced walls and its complicated group of central mountains. Langrenus is 85 miles in diameter, with walls which rise to 9,000 feet above the deepest part of the sunken floor. It lies on the edge of the Mare Fecunditatis, or Sea of Fertility.

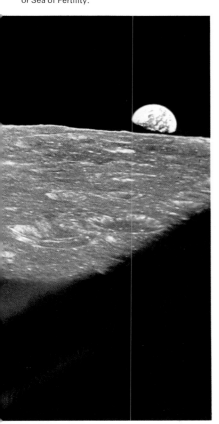

APOLLO 10

The Apollo 10 mission began on May 18, 1969, and ended with a perfect splashdown on May 26. It may aptly be described as a dress rehearsal for the manned landing with Apollo 11, inasmuch as its main objectives were to test the Lunar Module under lunar conditions, and to survey the Apollo 11 landing site—an area of the grey plain of the Mare Tranquillitatis (Sea of Tranquillity) not far from the crater Mőltke in relatively level country.

The Astronauts of Apollo 10

The Apollo 10 astronauts were Colonel Tom Stafford, Commander Eugene Cernan and Commander John Young. In every way they achieved everything that could have been expected of them —and they fulfilled their expressed aim of 'sharing their experiences', as they put it. All through the mission, even in its tensest moments, they kept up a running commentary upon what was happening and their vivid descriptions were enhanced by their invariable good humour and sense of fun.

For this mission there was, of course, no actual landing. The Lunar Module, known by its nickname of 'Snoopy', was separated from the Command Module, and brought down to within 10 miles of the lunar surface. The Lunar Module did not carry a television camera, and the two astronauts (Stafford and Cernan) concentrated upon taking film and still photographs of the Mare Tranquillitatis. The only serious hitch in the entire mission was that the cameras gave trouble during the closest approach, but the other pictures brought back were of superb quality, and showed the Moon's barren surface in greater detail than ever before.

The Moon from Close Range

Almost as soon as contact was re-established when the astronauts came out from 'behind' the Moon, having put themselves into lunar orbit, the first television pictures were received. The grey plain of the Mare Crisium, or Sea of Crises, stood out magnificently, together with parts of the Mare Fœcunditatis (Sea of Fertility) and Mare Smythii (Smyth's Sea). However, these parts of the Moon were in full sunlight, and it was when the spaceship approached the lunar terminator, or boundary between the daylit and night hemispheres, that the pictures became really spactacular. Landing Area 2, planned for Apollo 11, was seen in great detail. Beside the crater of Mőltke were two long rifts, the more prominent of which was nicknamed 'U.S. Highway 1'—a term that is likely to be retained, unofficially if not officially! Next came the rough uplands bordering the Mare Tranquillitatis, and an excellent view was obtained of the large crater Delambre, with its terraced walls. Equally fascinating were some of the smaller, relatively deep craters, notably Schmidt, with its bowl-shaped interior and deep shadow, and Theon Senior.

Earthrise over the Moon *(below)* as photographed by the astronauts of Apollo 10 in May 1969.

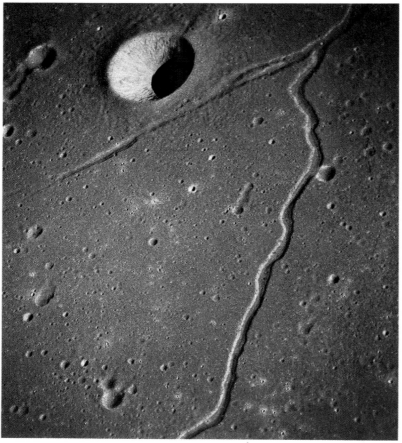

'The Diamond Back Rille' *(left)* Taken at an altitude of 60 nautical miles on the approach to Apollo Landing Site 2 in the Sea of Tranquillity, the picture shows the "Diamond Back Rille" connecting with an elongated crater. The top of the frame is orientated northeast. The circular crater is Maskelyne X (Map: 19) with a diameter of about 2 statute miles.

The Command Module *(above)* During the 'swoop' over the Sea of Tranquillity, Commander Young remained in the Command Module, while Colonel Stafford and Commander Cernan went on board the Lunar Module for their close approach to the Moon. The Command Module is seen here against the background of the lunar craters.

One of the most dramatic views of all was that of Godin, a crater more than 20 miles in diameter, with a floor that contained a massive central mountain together with ridges, depressions and hills. Then the space-ship passed on over the dark part of the Moon—to return to the sunlight when over the hemisphere which is always turned away from Earth. It was here that the astronauts saw at least two features which they described as 'perfect volcanoes', with blackened upper crater-bowls.

Circling the Moon

Altogether, Commander Young made 31 circuits of the Moon. It was his rôle to stay in the Command Module ('Charlie Brown') while Colonel Stafford and Commander Cernan made their swoop down over the Mare Tranquillitatis in the Lunar Module. Radio contact was maintained with the Lunar Module all the time, though there was a brief period when the astronauts' words became indistinct. Stafford and Cernan described the scene as almost unbelievable.

Landing Site 2 had been selected with great care. (Landing Site 1 is also on the Mare Tranquillitatis, but was not intended to be used for Apollo 11.) From what Stafford and Cernan saw, it proved to be very much as expected, and less rough than most other parts of the Moon, which is an important consideration; but no words can do justice to the grandeur of the scene. Also under study was Landing Site 3, on the Sinus Medii or Central Bay, the alternative selection for Apollo 11.

Jettisoning the Lunar Module

After Stafford and Cernan had fired the Lunar Module engines to return to the Command Module—not without incident, since there was a period of what Cernan described as 'a rough ride' before the separation of the two stages was effected—docking was carried out, and the upper stage of 'Snoopy' was jettisoned. Still the Command Module circled the Moon, and still the astronauts sent back descriptions of the fantastic scenes below them. Finally, the motors were brought into action once more, and the Moon started to recede; the television pictures sent back were unique, and over a period of minutes the Moon seemed to be racing away. When the lunar world had been left far behind, the astronauts were able to send back dramatic pictures of the Earth, with its continents, its oceans, and—needless to say—its clouds. Splashdown took place exactly as planned, and the Command Module was followed throughout its descent through the atmosphere before its parachutes opened and the astronauts came down in a relatively calm sea.

All the objects of Apollo 10 were achieved. Men had been closer to the Moon than ever before, and an official NASA spokesman summed matters up by saying that 'the mission was a 110 per cent success'.

The Far Side *(above right)*
This photograph taken from Apollo 10 Command Module on the far side of the moon shows Crater 302 (162 degrees east and 10 degrees south) from an altitude of 69 miles, looking south. The crater has a diameter of 115 miles and exhibits terracing and central peaks, features often seen on large craters on the front side.

Crater on the Far Side of the Moon *(lower right)*
Photographed at close range from 'Snoopy', the Lunar Module of Apollo 10, during Stafford and Cernan's descent to below 10 miles.

The Far Side *(overleaf)*
Apollo 10 photographed these lunar rough uplands whose craters are yet unnamed.

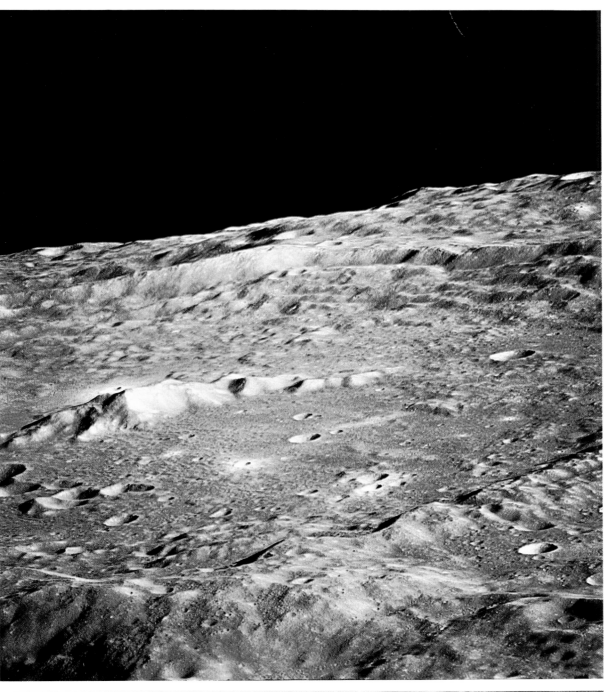

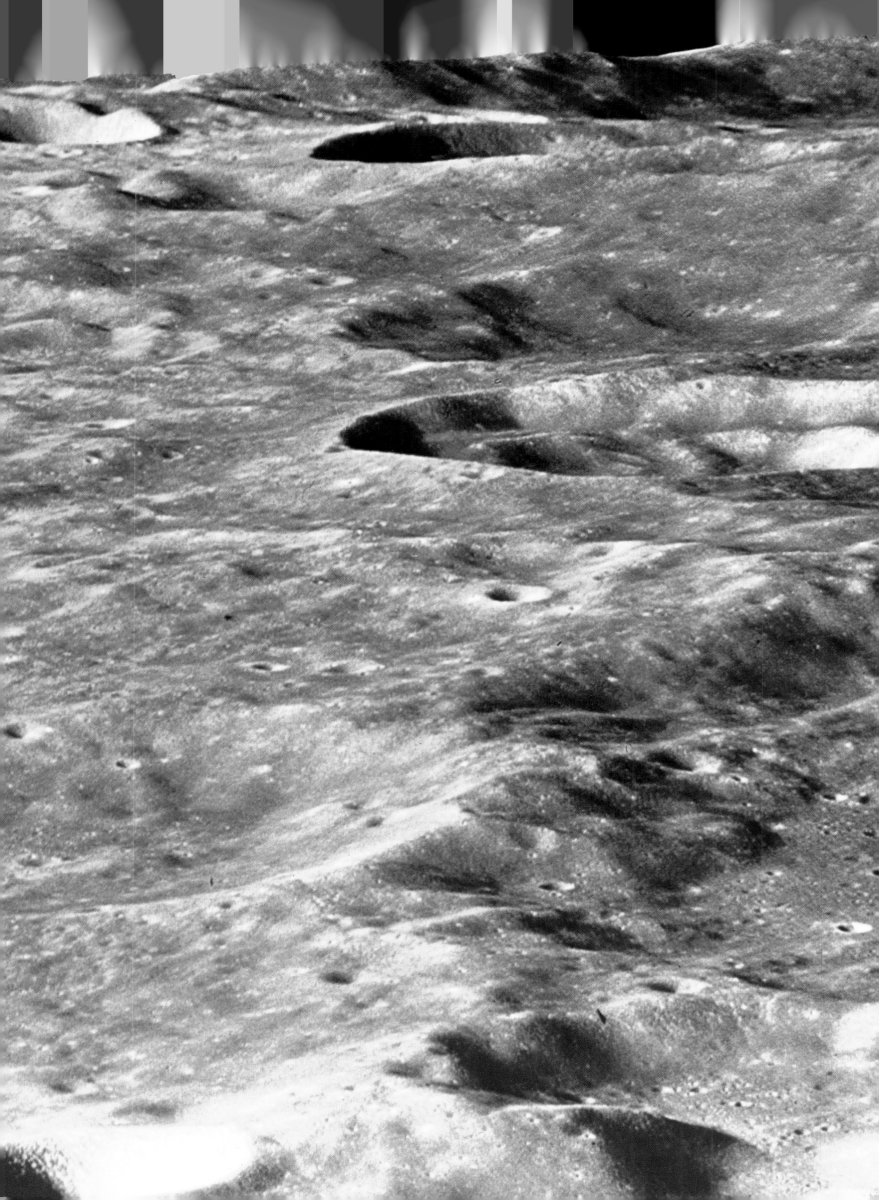

APOLLO 11: THE LANDING

The Giant Leap

"That's one small step for a man; a giant leap for mankind." Those words, never to be forgotten, were spoken by Neil Armstrong at 10.56 EDT on July 20th 1969, as he stepped out on to the surface of the Moon. Apollo 11 was a triumphant success; the dreams of twenty centuries had come true at last.

Apollo 11 had blasted away from Cape Kennedy on July 16th. The crew consisted of Astronaut Neil Armstrong, destined to be the first man on the Moon; Colonel Edwin Aldrin, who would accompany him on the lunar surface; and Lieutenant-Colonel Michael Collins, who would remain in the Command Module, orbiting at a height of approximately 60 miles above the Moon during the final stages of the expedition. There were no complications during the launching or during the trans-lunar flight: all the instruments functioned perfectly, communications were good, and all three astronauts were in excellent shape. Neither was there any trouble with the insertion into lunar orbit. Exactly on schedule, Apollo 11 was given the 'go' signal for the landing maneuver. This time there were no comic strip cartoon nicknames. The call sign for the Lunar Module was Eagle, and for the Command Module Columbia.

The Descent

The preparations followed the pattern set by Apollo 10. The Lunar Module had been inspected; Armstrong and Aldrin went into it, and prepared to blast away from the mother craft. The descent engine was fired at 10 per cent of its power for 15 seconds, and the throttle was then opened to 40 per cent of its full power. During this vital maneuver, Apollo 11 was on the far side of the Moon, and so out of touch with Mission Control; but when contact was re-established it was clear that all was well with Columbia and Eagle. (Diagram 1).

The descent engine burn for Descent Orbit Injection (DOI for short) was made under the guidance of the Lunar Module's, "electronic brain", PGNS (Primary Guidance and Navigation System), but Armstrong was able to keep track of events by means of his instruments. In particular, both he and Aldrin could consult the attitude indicator, which summarized all information about the Module's position in space. Any movement in pitch, roll or yaw was indicated at once, so it was always possible for the astronauts to take over control manually if need be. In case of sudden emergency, the ABORT button would have been pressed, and Eagle would have blasted back into orbit to rendezvous with Collins in the Command Module.

The DOI maneuver lowered the Module toward the Moon, until the height above the lunar surface was a mere 50,000 feet; at that moment the ground distance from the intended landing site was approximately 260 nautical miles (Diagram 2). Next, there began the powered descent initiation (PDI), using the descent engine to brake Eagle out of the descent transfer orbit. What had to be done, in fact, was to fire the engine against the direction of motion, slowing the Module down and reducing the velocity almost to zero for the start of the vertical descent. The braking maneuver ended at about 7,000 feet above the surface, and the Module was rotated to an upright windows-forward attitude. The start of the final approach phase was called the "high-gate" (Diagram 3), and the start of the landing phase, at only 500 feet, was called the "low-gate" (Diagram 4).

Still all went well, but everybody—the astronauts, Mission Control at Houston, and the millions of people watching their television screens at home — knew that the most dangerous moments of the entire mission were approaching.

Leaving the Earth (above)
The Earth, seen from over 100,000 miles during Apollo 11's outward journey to the Moon. Africa can be seen clearly, together with parts of Europe and Asia.

Approaching the Moon (below)
The approach to the landing-site in the Sea of Tranquillity is seen in this photograph. taken from the Lunar Module when it was still orbiting the Moon and was docked to the Command Module. The large crater is Maskelyne; the Hypatia Cleft (U.S.1) upper left centre, with Möltke to the right. The landing site is in the center, close to the edge of the sunlit area.

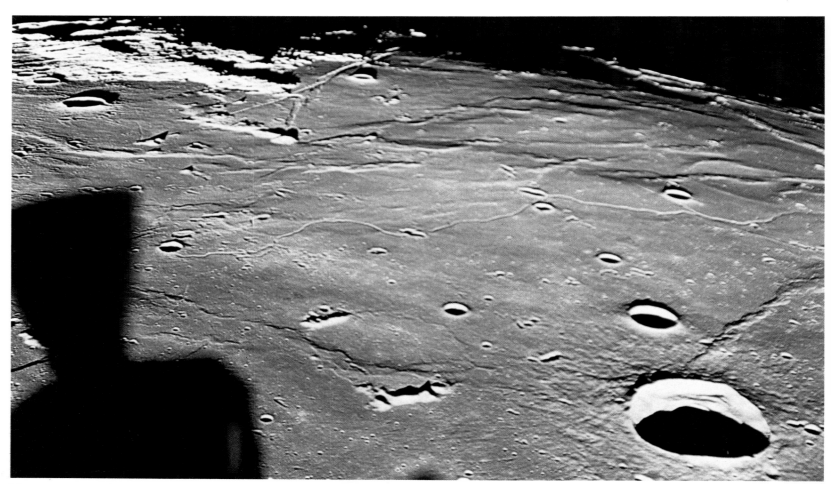

At low-gate, Armstrong took over manual control; the computers had done their work, and it was time for human intelligence and skill. Eagle was hovering at 500 feet above the Sea of Tranquillity, and it could continue there for only two minutes. Within that time, Armstrong had to make up his mind whether to go on down, or to fire the engine and blast back into orbit. There could be no second chance. If he and Aldrin were to land on the Moon, it must be now.

First, he had to check that the ground below was smooth, and free from boulders and pits. Armstrong had orders to "abort" if the tilt exceeded 6½ degrees. Since he could not see straight down through the space-craft, he had to tilt it as it hovered while he and Aldrin looked out of the windows. The manual control was delicate; on the instrument panel there were handles which allowed him to turn the module, or to shift it by using the thrust controller. In fact, the landing site below (0 deg. 41 m. 15s. North 23 deg. 26m. East) was 22,257 ft. West and 4,290 ft. North of the planned

Diagram 1 (below)
The diagram shows the procedure for the undocking of the Lunar Module from the Command Module, and the start of its moonward descent by the use of its own power. The LEM's descent orbit was calculated so that it would land in the Sea of Tranquillity close to the terminator (i.e. the boundary between the sunlit and night hemispheres of the Moon).

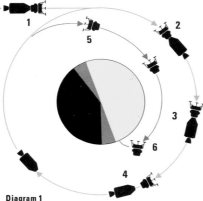

Diagram 1
1. Path from Earth. 2. Turns to tail-first position and fires into lunar orbit. 3. Correction to circular orbit. 4. LEM undocks. 5. Descent transfer orbit before final descent. 6. Descent begins.

landing ellipse centre since they had to avoid a boulder-strewn crater "about the size of a football pitch". Armstrong used the thrust control and Eagle moved slowly to one side above a smoother surface. The decision was made. All forward velocity was cancelled out, and Armstrong began the final descent at a rate of three feet per second. The engines were still working; had they faltered at that moment, disaster would have been complete.

At the last moments of descent, five-foot wires (lunar surface sensing probes) projecting from the Module's landing pads touched the surface. Lunar contact lights on the instrument panel flashed on. Exactly one second later, Armstrong shut off the descent engine by operating the thrust controller — and Eagle fell the last few feet, landing on the Sea of Tranquillity and coming to rest. The long journey was over, and after scarcely a pause Neil Armstrong reported: "Houston. Tranquillity Base here. The Eagle has landed."

Though the whole maneuver had been planned down to the last detail, it

had never been rehearsed under realistic conditions, simply because no rehearsal was possible. The Moon has no atmosphere, so that nothing in the way of a parachute could be used. Yet the touch down was faultless, a tribute not only to the efficiency of the computers and the engines, but also to the supreme courage and skill of Armstrong and Aldrin.

Their calm, level voices told the world that the first men on the Moon had arrived.

Diagram 2 (below)
Approaching the Moon. The orbit of the Command Module is shown, with its approximately constant height of more than 60 miles above the Moon; the path of the Lunar Module is also shown during the descent stage. PDI (Powered Descent Initiation) began at 260 miles, surface range, from the landing-site. At 235 miles the throttle was put to FTP (Fixed Throttle Position), and the Module then passed more or less over the conspicuous crater Maskelyne. Still descending, it reached the High-Gate position, ready for the final approach phase.

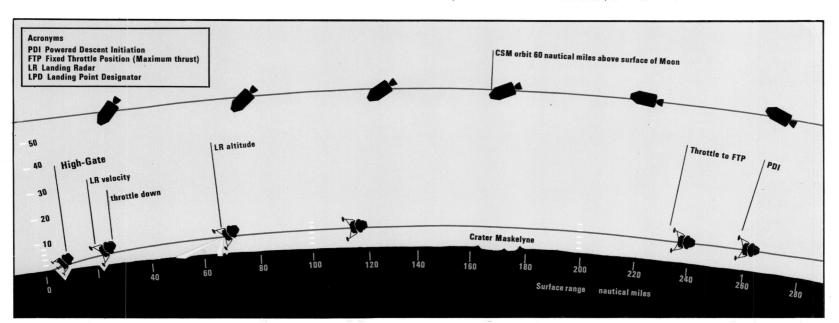

Acronyms
PDI Powered Descent Initiation
FTP Fixed Throttle Position (Maximum thrust)
LR Landing Radar
LPD Landing Point Designator

CSM orbit 60 nautical miles above surface of Moon

50 40 High-Gate
30 LR velocity
20 throttle down
10

LR altitude

Throttle to FTP   PDI

Crater Maskelyne

40   60   80   100   120   140   160   180   200   220   240   260   280
0

Surface range   nautical miles

Diagram 3 (right)
At High-Gate, the Module was positioned so that the astronauts could see the landing site. Needless to say, the radar readings were all-important; it was only during the very last moments that Armstrong took over manual control. The forward velocity had now been reduced to almost zero, so that the Module was descending slowly and "balancing" itself against gravity by means of its engine. When the height over the surface of the Moon was only 500 feet, at Low-Gate, there came the start of the most critical maneuver of all: the touch-down.

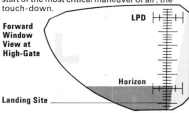

Forward Window View at High-Gate
LPD
Horizon
Landing Site

Diagram 4 (right)
With still very slight forward velocity, Eagle continued its descent, now under manual control. Armstrong could tilt the Module so as to see the Moon's surface through the window, and he maneuvered so as to avoid a crater which seemed to have too rocky an interior to be welcoming. At 150 feet he was satisfied that the surface below would be suitable as a landing-site, and he began the final descent, at a rate of 3 feet per second and nil forward velocity. At last the projecting foot-wires touched the Moon; the engines were cut, and Eagle touched down safely.

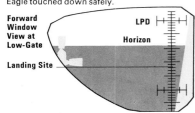

Forward Window View at Low-Gate
LPD
Horizon
Landing Site

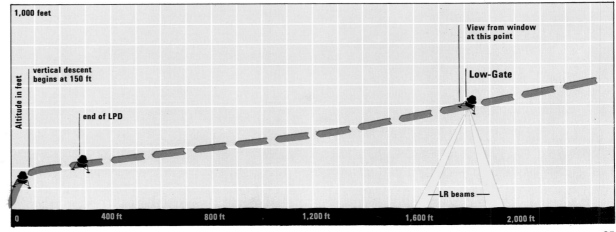

10,000 feet

Altitude in feet

High-Gate
View from window at this point
LR beams
Low-Gate

0   4,000 ft   8,000 ft   12,000 ft   16,000 ft   20,000 ft   24,000 ft

1,000 feet

Altitude in feet

View from window at this point

vertical descent begins at 150 ft

end of LPD

Low-Gate

LR beams

0   400 ft   800 ft   1,200 ft   1,600 ft   2,000 ft

APOLLO 11: MAN ON THE MOON

"Magnificent desolation." That was how Edwin Aldrin summed up the lunar scene when he was actually standing on the Sea of Tranquillity. He and Armstrong had less than three hours in which to carry out the whole of their scientific objectives planned during their Moon-walk, or, in NASA language, E.V.A. (Extra Vehicular Activity), and it proved to be all too short.

Armstrong stepped on to the lunar surface at 10.56 EDT on July 20. The first all-important task was to collect some samples of Moon-rocks, and this he began immediately – just in case some unexpected crisis made it necessary to make quick preparations for blast-off. In the event, all went well; Armstrong made his preliminary sample collection, and Aldrin joined him on the Moon's surface at 11.14 EDT, July 20. The next step was to move the television camera to a suitable position, and to begin the setting-up of the scientific experiments.

The first of these was the solar wind experiment, designed to collect particles sent out by the Sun. Solar wind is made up of low-energy particles emitted by the Sun in all directions. The Moon, having no atmosphere to shield it, is bombarded by these particles, and is an ideal place from which to measure them. The collector was unrolled at 11.35 and taken down at 1.52 EDT, July 21.

The Bulk Sample Collection

Next came the start of the bulk sample collection – certainly the most important of all the scientific objectives of E.V.A. Armstrong gave a description of the surface almost as soon as he had stepped out: "The surface is fine and powdery . . . I can pick it up loosely with my toe. It does adhere in fine layers like powdered charcoal to the sole and sides of my boots. I can only go in a small fraction of an inch." Later, he said: "Where I plug in the contingency sample collector I run into a very hard surface, but it appears to be very cohesive material of the same sort . . ." And later still: "These boulders look like basalt, and they probably have 2% whiter minerals in them." Aldrin commented on a surprising lack of penetration of all four of the feet pads of the lunar module. The astronauts collected 70 lbs of material in all.

The Laser Mirror and Seismometer

The third piece of equipment was a mirror composed of special crystals to reflect laser beams sent out from the Earth, and so provide exact information about the Moon's distance from us. It is hoped to cut measurement errors down to less than an inch by means of this device.

Finally, the astronauts set up a seismometer to measure what might be called 'moonquakes'. As soon as it had been erected, the seismometer began to send back data. It recorded the tremors due to the astronaut's own activity and also the blast-off of the ascent stage of the Lunar Module when Armstrong and Aldrin left the Moon. During the following days the remaining descent stage of the Module was heated up by the Sun, and internal movements took place in its material: all of these were recorded by the seismometer.

But there was also activity which did not seem to be man-made. On the early morning of July 23rd there came a record of what seemed to be the first genuine 'moonquake' ever measured by man. Evidently the Moon is less inactive than some theorists had supposed.

Man on the Moon *(right)*
One of the most dramatic photographs of the entire expedition. Aldrin stands on the Sea of Tranquillity, and the Module is reflected in the transparent facepiece of his helmet. This photograph was taken by Neil Armstrong.

The Lunar Scene *(above)*
From the window of the Lunar Module, the lunar scene was one of absolute desolation; the Sea of Tranquillity proves to be a plain, pitted with craters and strewn with boulders. There was color in the rocky surface; the sky was black even though the Sun was 10 degrees above the horizon.

The Descent
When Neil Armstrong became the first man on the Moon, he was being watched by millions of people on Earth. His descent down the ladder was seen on television, and he was in full radio communication both with Aldrin,

inside the Lunar Module, and with Mission Control in Houston. The left-hand picture shows him descending the ladder; a few seconds later he stepped out on to the Moon's surface, as shown in the right-hand photograph.

Aldrin on the Moon
Colonel Edwin Aldrin became the second man on the Moon within half an hour of Armstrong's descent. Like Armstrong, he was quick to adapt himself to the low lunar gravity and was soon at work.

The Lunar Crust

The first, and most important, discovery made by Armstrong and Aldrin was that the Moon's surface was hard. The foot-pads of the Module showed no tendency to sink, and the astronauts walked out on to a surface that showed no indications of being treacherous. Their footprints were visible, but were depressed only a fraction of an inch; the amount of dust was slight. The material seemed to be cohesive, and to give the impression of being slippery. Sample collecting presented no problems, and some 70 pounds of lunar material were brought back home for analysis.

When the samples were first opened — in a vacuum chamber, need-less to say — they were found to be coated with blackish "powder", and it was not until the quarantining process had been completed that any reliable analysis could be made. The main surprise was the amount of glassy, crystalline material; the rock itself gave every indication of being igneous, and of basaltic nature. The color of the material was described as ranging from dark brown through yellow and yellowish-brown, while the lunar dust from the core samples showed up as grey, though under certain lighting conditions there was a brownish cast. The dust itself was very loose.

No evidence was found to support the idea that the lunar maria had once been true seas, filled with water. Neither was there any immediate

The Flag *(left)*
Colonel Aldrin with the Stars and Stripes which
had been set up in the Sea of Tranquillity – as
photographed by Neil Armstrong. The flag is
motionless; with no atmosphere, and therefore
no wind, there is nothing to disturb it.

Shadows on the Moon *(below)*
One feature of the Moon is the blackness of its
shadows. With no atmosphere, the shadows
are jet-black, and contrast with the glaring
brilliance of the sunlit landscape. These

photographs show the effect well; the shadows
of the Module and of Aldrin are thrown on to
the rocks. The pictures were taken by
Armstrong with a hand-held camera.

The Plaque *(below)*
When they left the Module and came out on to
the lunar surface, the two astronauts brought
with them a plaque, bearing a message of peace.
This was left behind on the Moon when Eagle
took off to rendezvous with Columbia.

evidence of meteoritic material, but a relatively high percentage of titanium, as compared with many terrestrial rocks favoured the idea of volcanic activity in the past. All these results, together with the records sent back by the seismometer, led the investigators to the conclusion that the Moon's crust had a depth of about 12 miles, and that there must be a great deal of internal heat.

Evidently the Moon did not have a "cold" origin, as some authorities had supposed.

Past Life on the Moon?

There had been considerable speculation as to the possibility of finding traces of past life on the Moon. Virtually none of the investigators had any faith in this attractive idea – and so

it proved; none of the rocks showed any evidence of organic material, and there were certainly no "fossils". Quarantining was rigorously carried out; mice were injected with lunar dust to see if any ill-effects could be noted, but, predictably, nothing happened. Everything pointed to the fact that the Moon has always been sterile, and that no life had ever existed there before

Armstrong and Aldrin made their historic descent on July 20, 1969.

It would be unwise to claim that the Sea of Tranquillity is typical of all parts of the Moon, but it is very likely that the rocks in other maria are of similar basic type and chemical composition. Future Apollo landings will show whether any marked differences occur from one region to another.

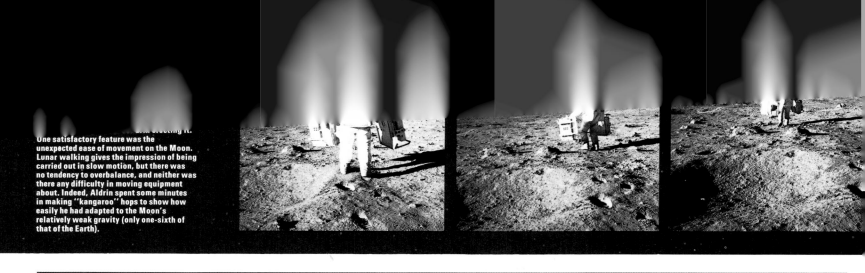

One satisfactory feature was the unexpected ease of movement on the Moon. Lunar walking gives the impression of being carried out in slow motion, but there was no tendency to overbalance, and neither was there any difficulty in moving equipment about. Indeed, Aldrin spent some minutes in making ''kangaroo'' hops to show how easily he had adapted to the Moon's relatively weak gravity (only one-sixth of that of the Earth).

Moonquakes

One of the most important of the experiments carried out by Armstrong and Aldrin during their Moon-walk was the setting up of the seismometer. There was nothing particularly revolutionary about the design of the instrument, which was essentially similar to a seismometer intended for use on Earth; but there was no general agreement as to whether or not any "moonquakes" would be recorded.

In fact, the seismometer began transmitting information at once. The early records were not significant, because they related to the movements of the astronauts themselves, and subsequently — after blast-off — to distortions in the remaining part of the Module which had been left on the Moon. Predictably, these disturbances soon died away, and it became possible to study records of tremors originating in the Moon itself. One record seemed to be much too strong to be due to anything but a true seismic disturbance; a meteoritic impact would have been much too much of a coincidence.

Then, on July 25, fourteen unusual seismic events were recorded simultaneously on the short-period and the long-period vertical seismometers. Apparently they were caused by landslides in nearby craters, triggered off by the expansion in the rocky materials due to the increasing heat as the Sun rose high in the lunar sky. (Lunar noon at the landing site occurred on July 27.) The tremors were slight, but it had been calculated that the lunar seismometers would be more than ten times as sensitive as any comparable equipment on the surface of the Earth.

Calculations could be made with respect to the more violent "moonquakes", and in one case it was estimated that the surface wave had been generated at a distance of some 2,300 miles across the Moon. The records indicated a layered structure, with a crust about 12 miles thick. However, any tremors on the Moon must be slight by terrestrial standards, and are certainly not strong enough to present a hazard to future manned expeditions there. Really violent lunar activity belongs to the remote past.

It had been hoped that the seismometer would keep on working for two years. Before long it was found that the temperature of the instrument was between 45° and 60°F. higher than had been expected, probably because excessive heating of the seismic package by the Lunar Module's ascent engine plume degraded the thermal surfaces of the equipment. However, the early records at least were very clear and informative, and provided new information as to the character of the Moon's crust. All future Apollo astronauts will take seismometers with them, and within the next few years we should have a really adequate knowledge of the Moon's crust and internal structure.

Solar Wind Experiment *(above)*
The first experiment to be set up during the astronauts' E.V.A. was the screen to collect information about what is termed solar wind — made up of low-energy particles sent out by the Sun in all directions. The Moon's lack of atmosphere means that the solar wind can reach the surface unhindered. The "collecting screen" was dismantled before the astronauts went back inside the Module, and was brought back home for study.

The Laser Mirror *(below)*
Another experiment was that of erecting a special screen with a highly reflecting surface. The aim was to use laser beams from Earth, which would be reflected in the screen; in this way very exact measures of the Earth-Moon distance would be possible. The laser screen was left on the Moon, and within a few days the first reflections had been successfully received.

APOLLO 11: RETURN JOURNEY

Lift Off

Landing on the Moon had been hazardous, because there were so many unknown factors. The subsequent lift off back to orbit was expected to be straightforward, but it was just as tense, because everything depended on the correct functioning of the single engine of the ascent stage of the Lunar Module. If it failed, there could be no rescue operation: Collins, in the circling Command Module, was unable to attempt a landing on the lunar surface.

Following a rest period, Armstrong and Aldrin prepared to blast off. Exactly on schedule, they fired the engine – and it worked perfectly. It burned for 7 minutes 14 seconds, and sent the upper part of the Eagle back to rendezvous with the waiting Columbia (see diagram). The lower part of the Lunar Module was left on the Moon, together with the American flag, the laser reflector, the seismometer, the emblems, and the items which the astronauts had discarded.

Rendezvous with Columbia

The next step was to rendezvous and dock with Columbia; and it was here that the astronauts experienced their first and only unexpected crisis. During docking there were uncontrollable movements of Eagle which led to a temporary loss of contact with Mission Control. Fortunately, the crisis was brief; after a few minutes the docking maneuver was carried out, and before long Aldrin and Armstrong were back inside the Command Module with their precious cargo of lunar samples. Eagle, its work done, was despatched into space.

The Journey Home

On July 22nd there came the last 'lunar maneuver' – the engine burn behind the Moon that put Apollo back into a homeward path. The return journey was comparatively uneventful, and some-

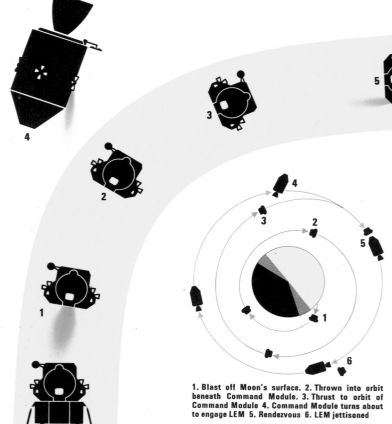

1. Blast off Moon's surface. 2. Thrown into orbit beneath Command Module. 3. Thrust to orbit of Command Module 4. Command Module turns about to engage LEM 5. Rendezvous 6. LEM jettisoned

thing in the nature of an anti-climax right up until splashdown in the Pacific at 12 hours 50 minutes EDT on July 24th, thirteen miles away from the waiting recovery ship, the U.S.S. Hornet, when the Command Module hit the sea upside down and had to be righted.

On this occasion there were no red-carpet ceremonies for the astronauts, because of the need for immediate and strict quarantining. They left the capsule in their contamination suits, boarded a raft, and were taken up into a helicopter. As soon as they reached the Hornet they went into a quarantine trailer, and it was while they were inside that Richard Nixon, President of the United States, addressed them for the second time. The astronauts could be

seen behind their window, but were completely isolated and would remain so for the next eighteen days.

Quarantine

Many people felt that the quarantine restrictions were too strict, but the NASA authorities were entirely justified. Even though the Moon is almost certainly a sterile world, there is always a million-to-one chance that contact with lunar material may involve as yet unknown hazards for Man–and a single mistake would be one too many. The rocks brought back were also strictly quarantined before being sent out for analysis in scientific laboratories.

Man had achieved his greatest triumph. The First Men on the Moon were home.

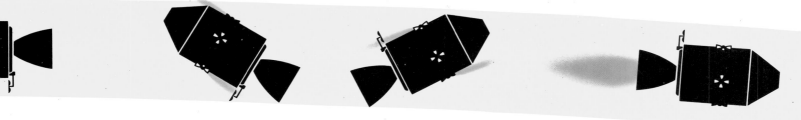

The First Men on the Moon

Neil Armstrong, commander of Apollo 11, was born in Wapakoneta, Ohio, on August 5, 1930. In 1955, joined NASA as an aeronautical research pilot. He was selected as an astronaut in 1962, and commanded the Gemini 8 mission, carrying out the first orbital docking maneuver. He is married, with two sons.

Edwin Aldrin, known by his nickname of 'Buzz'', was born in Montclair, N.J., on January 20, 1930. He carried out his first space mission with Gemini 12 ; he had been selected as an astronaut in 1963. Colonel Aldrin has the reputation of being the best scientist of all the astronauts, and has a doctorate from the Massachusetts Institute of Technology, He is married, with two sons and a daughter.

Michael Collins, a Lieutenant-Colonel in the U.S. Air Force, was born in Rome in 1930 (October 31), but is of course purely American. He was selected as an astronaut in 1963, and flew in Gemini 10, launched on July 18, 1966 ; during that mission he undertook two 'space-walks''. It was typical of him that he was very ready to concede the honour of an actual Moon-landing to his colleagues, while he carried out the equally essential rôle of Command Module pilot. He, too, is married, and has one son and two daughters.

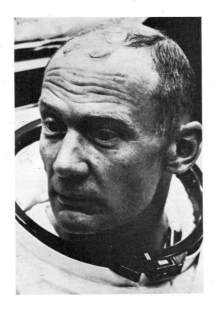

FUTURE APOLLO LANDING AREAS

Even before Armstrong, Aldrin, and Collins blasted off from Cape Kennedy on July 16th 1969, the Apollo planners had made a list of sites for the next nine landings. The choice was bound to be provisional, and subject to alteration in the light of what Apollo 11 brought home, but the list was made as varied as possible. It was inevitable that the first landing should be in the nature of a reconnaisance; Armstrong and Aldrin made only a brief foray on to the surface of the Moon, and at no time did they move far from their Lunar Module.

But their prime research task was, as we have seen, geological – to bring back material to find out the nature of the lunar surface, leading on to a better knowledge of the history of the Solar System and the Universe itself. The objective behind the first selection of the next Apollo sites was thus primarily to develop knowledge of lunar geology as extensively and with as much variety as possible. The Apollo planners knew that our knowledge of the Moon will remain incomplete until samples of the lunar crust can be brought back from all kinds of areas – for it is premature to claim that one part of the Moon's surface must be the same as another.

The choice of the Sea of Tranquillity (Map: pp. 16-17) for the pioneer Apollo was dictated largely by safety considerations. On the western hemisphere of the Moon, the huge Oceanus Procellarum, or Ocean of Storms (Map: pp. 16-17), appeared almost as suitable.

On the provisional list given by NASA authorities, there were further potential landing sites near the crater Flamsteed (Map: pp. 16-17), in the hills not far from Marius (Map: pp. 16-17), and near the spectacular winding valley to the north west of Aristarchus, known as Schröter's Valley (Map: pp. 14-15) in honor of the German astronomer who discovered it nearly two hundred years ago. The latter area is of special geological interest, and may tell us much more about the history of the Moon. Aristarchus itself is the brightest crater on the Moon, and is particularly subject to the reddish glows and obscurations known as 'TLPs' or Transient Lunar Phenomena (page 12).

Also on the NASA list were sites near the bright crater Censorinus (Map: pp. 16-17) in the highlands bordering the Mare Tranquillitatis; near Fra Mauro (Map: pp. 16-17) in the Mare Nubium; near Littrow (Map: pp. 14-15), a bay on the edge of the Mare Serenitatis; and in an area close to the Hyginus Cleft (Map: pp. 14-15) in the Mare Vaporum.

It was also proposed to attempt landings in or near the ray craters Tycho (Map: pp. 18-19) in the southern uplands, and Copernicus (Map: pp. 16-17) just south of the Carpathian Mountains. There can be little doubt that ray craters are 'young', and samples from them would be of immense interest, but unfortunately the dangers of touching down there are obviously much greater than in a comparatively smooth Mare. It remains to be seen whether the later modules will be sufficiently tough and manœuvrable.

Eventually, there may be landings on the far side of the Moon – but certainly not yet, as Mission Control would be out of touch and the astronauts would be hopelessly cut off. A landing on the far side must await the establishment of a chain of communications satellites in orbit round the Moon. Then, too, it will be time to consider the site for the first permanent scientific base on the Moon. NASA has predicted the establishment of such a base before 1980.

Tycho *Orbiter 5*

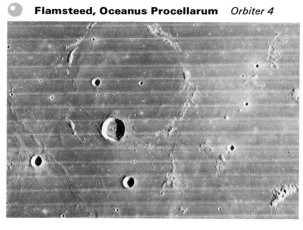

Flamsteed, Oceanus Procellarum *Orbiter 4*

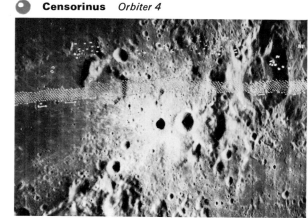

Censorinus *Orbiter 4*

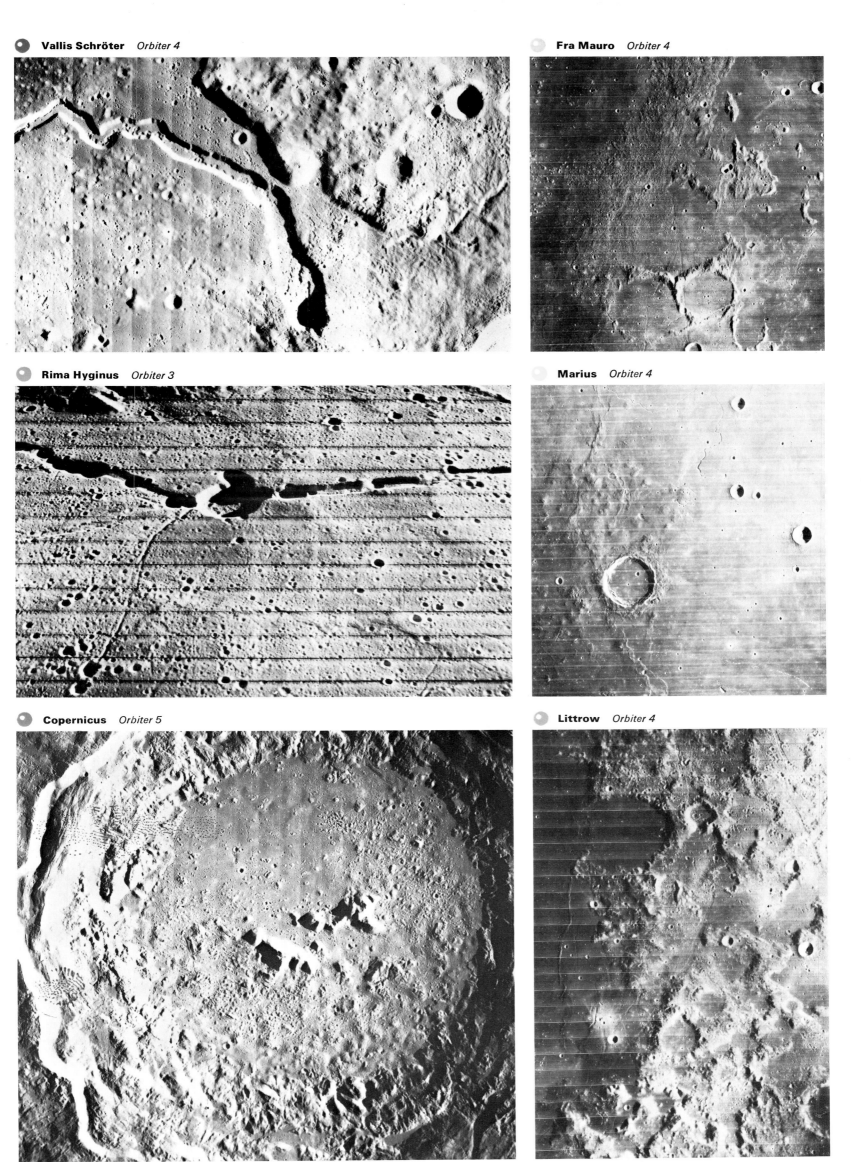

Vallis Schröter *Orbiter 4*

Fra Mauro *Orbiter 4*

Rima Hyginus *Orbiter 3*

Marius *Orbiter 4*

Copernicus *Orbiter 5*

Littrow *Orbiter 4*

WHERE NEXT? MARS

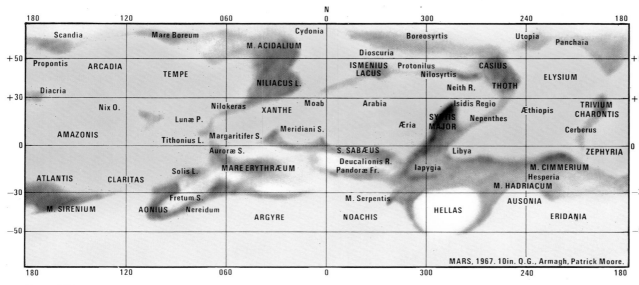

MARS, 1967. 10in. O.G., Armagh, Patrick Moore.

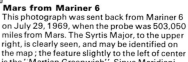

Mars from Mariner 6
This photograph was sent back from Mariner 6 on July 29, 1969, when the probe was 503,050 miles from Mars. The Syrtis Major, to the upper right, is clearly seen, and may be identified on the map ; the feature slightly to the left of center is the ' Martian Greenwich'', Sinus Meridiani (longtitude 0 degrees). The southern polar cap is excellently shown, and there are indications of whiteness also in the far north.

Map of Mars
This map, on Mercator's projection, shows the main features of Mars visible with a telescope of moderate size. It was compiled by Patrick Moore from his observations made in 1967 with the 10 in. refractor at Armagh Observatory. North is at the top – following the American custom, as opposed to astronomical practice. The most prominent features are the Syrtis Major in the equatorial region, and the Mare Acidalium in the northern hemisphere.

Venus or Mars ?

Now that the Moon has been reached, it is time to look further afield. Two planets are within range : Venus, closer to the Sun than we are, and Mars, which is further away.

The surface conditions on Venus, discovered by the American and Russian space probes and described on page 6, effectively preclude any manned landings there in the forseeable future. Not so with Mars, which, though forbidding in many respects, is a practicable and fascinating proposition. Mars must therefore be our next target.

Mars Data

Mars has a diameter of 4200 miles, so that in size it is intermediate between the Moon and the Earth. It has an appreciable atmosphere, and has always been regarded as a likely abode of life. Its climate is much cooler than that of the Earth, because it is further from the Sun ; its mean distance is 141,500,000 miles, as opposed to Earth's 93,000,000. At its closest Mars can approach us to within 35,000,000 miles, so that it is then about 150 times as far away as the Moon. The Martian year amounts to 687 days, while the rotation period is 24 hours 37 minutes – roughly half an hour longer than ours. The tilt of the axis is much the same as that of the Earth, so that the seasons are of the same basic type, though they are, of course, much longer. The surface gravity is relatively low ; a man who weighs 150 lbs on Earth would weigh a mere 50 lbs on Mars.

Through a telescope, Mars shows definite markings, which are permanent surface features and which have been carefully mapped. First, there are the white caps which cover the poles ; it is tempting to regard them as ice-caps, but there can be no true analogy with the deep snowy caps which cover the poles of Earth. From the rate at which the Martian caps shrink in the spring and early summer, and the tiny amount of moisture which they release into the atmosphere, it is clear that they must be very thin. Their depth cannot be so much as one foot, and is more probably less than one inch.

The dark areas are characteristic, and seem to be to all intents and purposes permanent. The most prominent of them, the V-shaped region known as the Syrtis Major, was first drawn by Christiaan Huygens more than 300 years ago, and has not changed since then. Originally the dark areas were thought to be seas, but this attractive theory had to be given up as soon as it became obvious that Mars is desperately short of water. Alternatively, it was suggested that they might be due to organic matter – or, using the term in a broad sense, "vegetation" It is true that there are seasonal changes on Mars, affecting the dark areas and linked with the shrinking of the polar caps, which might well be due to the growth of Martian organisms with the arrival of moisture wafted from the poles.

Much of the surface is reddish-ochre in hue. The Martian "deserts", to give them their common name, are not in the least like the deserts of Earth ; for one thing, they are extremely cold, and at night their temperature, even at the equator, must fall to below −100 degrees Fahrenheit. Neither are they likely to be made up of sand, and are more probably coated with some reddish mineral.

Rockets to Mars

Before the launching of the first planetary probes, it was thought that conditions on Mars might not be too severe. Admittedly, the climate was chilly, and the temperature could never rise to more than about 80 degrees Fahrenheit, while the nights were bitter ; neither was the atmosphere breathable. However, Mars appeared much more friendly than the Moon, and the chances of underground water supplies could not be ruled out.

Then, in 1965, the American probe Mariner 4 by-passed Mars and sent back the first detailed photographs. The results came as something of a surprise. Instead of being flat, Mars proved to be crater-scarred ; its surface was not unlike that of the Moon. though there was considerable evidence of erosion. To make matters worse, the atmosphere proved to be much thinner than had been expected, and to be composed chiefly of carbon dioxide.

Though Mariner 4 was a success, it sent back only a few good pictures, and astronomers eagerly awaited the results from Mariners 6 and 7, launched in 1969. Neither was scheduled to land on Mars. Mariner 6 was destined to 'fly-by' over the planet's equator, while Mariner 7 was to pass over the pole ; in each case the closest approach would be some 2,000 miles, and it was hoped that very detailed photographs would be obtained. In the event, both probes functioned excellently, and results were spectacular by any standards.

The main features were, of course, the craters, which seemed to cover all

Mars from Mariner 6 : Picture 22
This narrow-angle view of Mars spans 52 miles E-W by 45 miles N-S. The large crater to the south (at the bottom of the picture) is 15 miles in diameter ; the irregular terrain to the N.W. of this crater is débris near the rim of a much larger crater over 150 miles across, shown in Picture 21. The local time was one hour before sunset. The photograph was taken on July 30, 1969, with Mariner at 2,150 miles from Mars.

Mars from Mariner 6 : Picture 18
One of the most striking photographs ever obtained from a space-probe. It was taken on July 30, 1969 during a twenty-minute period at Mariner's closest approach to the planet.

The narrow-angle picture extends 63 miles E-W by 48 miles N-S. The large crater, 24 miles in diameter, shows several slump terraces and radial gullies on the south wall ; the younger crater on the wall shows a central peak.

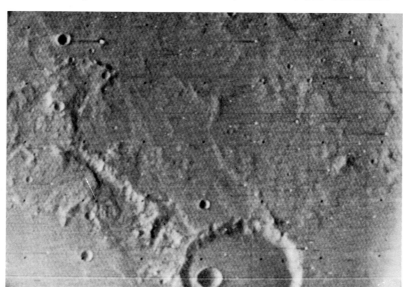

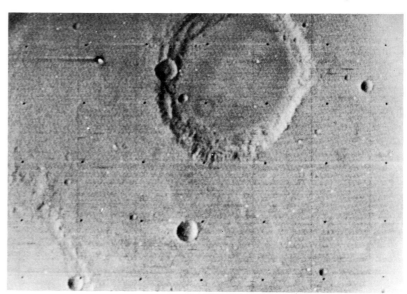

The Size of Mars

Though Mars is often called 'the second Earth', it is a considerably smaller globe. Its diameter is little more than half that of the world; but since there are no seas, the land area is about equal to that of Earth. The mean density of the globe is less, and the absence of any measurable magnetic field seems to indicate that there is no comparable heavy core. In size, Mars is roughly intermediate between the Earth and the Moon.

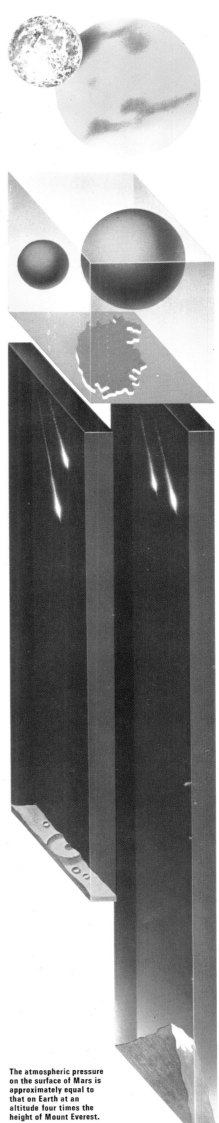

The Moons of Mars

Phobos and Deimos, the two moons of Mars, were discovered in 1877 by the American astronomer Asaph Hall at Washington. Phobos is perhaps about ten miles in diameter, Deimos about half this size. They are here shown in comparison to the island of Malta.

Phobos, the inner moon, moves at only 3,700 miles above the Martian surface, or approximately 5,800 miles from the planet's center. It completes one revolution in a mere 7 hours 39 minutes, which is much less than the length of the Martian day. To an observer on Mars, Phobos would seem to rise in the West and set in the East, taking only 4½ hours to cross the horizon and going through more than half its cycle of phases; it would do this three times a day.

Deimos, at 12,500 miles from the surface, has a period of 30 hours 18 minutes, so that it behaves differently. As Mars 'spins', Deimos almost keeps pace with it, and the interval between rising and setting would be 2½ Martian days.

Both satellites would appear too small and faint to be a useful source of illumination at night. Deimos, indeed, would look like nothing more than a large, dim, star. Also there would be long periods when they would be eclipsed by the shadow of Mars. And because their orbits lie practically in the place of the planet's equator, they would never be visible from high Martian latitudes. Nothing is known about their composition, but they certainly seem different in nature from our Moon. They may well be asteroids which were captured by Mars in the remote past.

The Martian Atmosphere

Mars has an escape velocity of 3.1 miles per second. This is enough for it to retain a considerable atmosphere, and before the first space probes were despatched most astronomers believed that this atmosphere must be made up chiefly of nitrogen. Oxygen and water vapor were expected to be in short supply: the ground pressure was estimated at around 85 millibars. The general view among astronomers was that at the surface of Mars the atmospheric pressure would be equal to the pressure in our own air at a height of about 53,000 feet above sea level.

The Mariner 4 flight of 1965 caused a sudden change of view. As the probe went behind Mars as seen from Earth, there was a brief period when its signals were coming to us through the Martian atmosphere – and it appeared that the density was much less than had been thought. Nowadays the pressure is estimated at less than 8 millibars at surface level on Mars, equivalent to that of our air at a height of over 100,000 feet. This is a depressing discovery as it means that the Martian atmosphere is not likely to be effective as a radiation screen in which case the surface of the planet will be unprotected. There is a growing body of opinion that the whole planet is radiation-soaked and sterile.

Clouds are often observed. They are of two kinds: high altitude 'white' clouds, possibly made up of ice crystals, and low-level 'yellow' clouds, which may be dust storms. Certainly there are no clouds capable of producing rainfall. There are no seas or lakes on Mars.

The poles are covered with whitish caps, which shrink during the Martian spring and almost vanish in summer. They are usually thought to be made up of a very thin layer of some icy or frosty deposit, though it is also possible that they consist of 'dry ice' – solid carbon dioxide. The results from the Mariner probes of 1969 confirmed that carbon dioxide is the main constituent of the atmosphere. A small amount of atomic oxygen was detected, but there was no clear evidence of any nitrogen, which must be in extremely short supply. Water vapor too is very scarce. The best that can be said about the Martian atmosphere is that it is not lethal, and that it may well be an adequate screen against meteors even if not against radiations.

The atmospheric pressure on the surface of Mars is approximately equal to that on Earth at an altitude four times the height of Mount Everest.

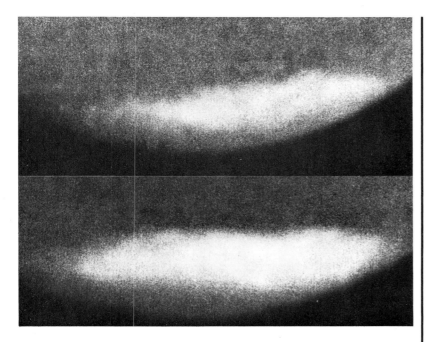

The Southern Polar Cap from Mariner 6
Enlarged photographs of the southern polar cap of Mars, obtained when Mariner was still thousands of miles from the planet. During this period (July 29, 1969) the southern Martian hemisphere was having its winter season. The polar cap was large and prominent. Note the irregularities in the northern boundary.

the regions of Mars which were surveyed. Some of the craters were huge; the feature known as Nix Olympica proved to be an enclosure more than 300 miles across. Others were small, and in every way the general impression was of a surface very much like that of a somewhat eroded Moon. The southern polar cap was seen in detail, and proved to have a somewhat irregular rim, indicating the presence there of hills and valleys. Haze was recorded over it, and the infra-red spectra of light reflected from the planet's surface seemed to show that there were ice crystals, presumably from an ice fog. Mars might be dry, but the Mariners led to the conclusion that a certain amount of water must exist there.

Life on Mars?

Mars had always been regarded as the one world in the Solar System, apart from the Earth, where life might exist. During the late 19th and early 20th centuries, Percival Lowell, the American astronomer who founded the famous observatory at Flagstaff, championed the theory that the strange, straight lines across Mars known conventionally as "canals" were in fact artificial waterways, built by the Martians to convey water from the icy poles through to the arid regions near the equator. As knowledge grew, Lowell's canal theory had fallen into disfavor; and, as had been expected, the Mariner pictures showed no signs of anything which might be interpreted as artificial. However, it is quite likely that some of the so-called canals are due to chains of craters.

Whether the dark areas are due to organic material is still a matter for dispute, but there is nothing improbable in the idea. The main drawback to it is that the thin atmosphere seems to be ineffective as a screen against harmful radiations coming from space. Before long, the matter should be cleared up. The successes with Mariners 6 and 7 have opened the way to further exploration of Mars; during the early 1970s it is planned to put probes into orbits round the planet, and a soft landing with an automatic vehicle is planned as part of the Viking program for 1973. The NASA authorities have claimed that it should be possible to put a man on Mars by 1985. This is by no means improbable, but long before then we should have found out whether the Red Planet is utterly sterile, or whether it is a world supporting lowly forms of life.

Mars from Mariner 6: Picture 21
Another photograph taken on July 30, 1969 when Mariner was almost at its closest to Mars, and was a mere 2,150 miles above the planet's surface. The area shown measures about 560 miles by 430 miles. The largest crater visible, in the south-east part of the picture, is rather over 150 miles in diameter; there are many others, and the impression is strikingly similar to the surface of the Moon.

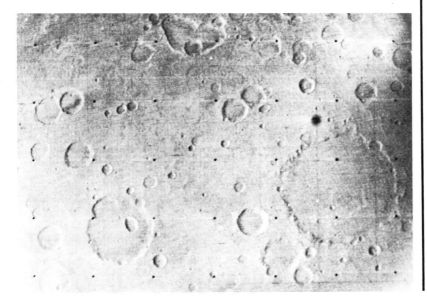

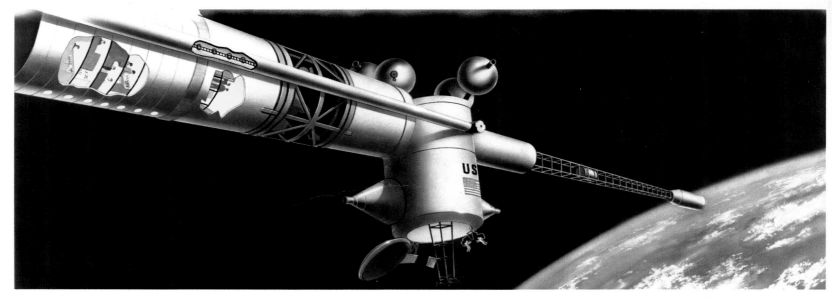

Into the Future

Now that men have reached the Moon, and successful probes have been sent to Mars and Venus, it is time to consider the future. There are various urgent problems to be borne in mind. In particular, there is the risk of contamination; if Earth bacteria were carried to Mars they might well destroy any life there, and there might also be the danger of bringing harmful substances back to our own world. The danger is less for Venus, and less still for the Moon, but strict precautions must always be taken. Eventually, no doubt, permanent bases will be set up on the lunar and Martian surfaces at least.

Yet it may also be that a space-station will be put into orbit round the Earth, to be permanently manned and used as a scientific laboratory and research base. A design released in June 1969 by the American authorities provides for a station 715 feet long, spinning at 3½ revolutions per minute to create artificial gravity. Whether this design will be adopted remains to be seen, but at any rate we cannot doubt that the next few years will see the setting-up of elaborate space-stations of various kinds.

INDEX

ACKNOWLEDGMENTS

The author and publishers gratefully acknowledge the kind help and assistance of: The Director and staff of the National Aeronautics and Space Administration in Houston, and particularly Mr Karl Hart, head of the Public Affairs Department, Mr S. M. Eulman, and Mr Haxton who made the photographs from Apollo 11 available to us in Houston; William A. Dunn of the US Information Service in London; Rand McNally Inc and particularly Mr Sanford Cobb and Mr Paul Tiddens; Hallwag AG and particularly Dr Peter Meyer and Mr Werner Merkli; The British Broadcasting Corporation and particularly the staff of "The Sky at Night"; Lutterworth Press and particularly Mr Michael Foxell; Miss Adrianne Bowles; Dr G. Fielder; Mr Kenneth Gatland; Mr William Dennison; Mr Hans van Hoorn; and Mr Francis Mildner.

Photographs have been supplied by: Mount Wilson and Palomar Observatory (p. 5), The Royal Astronomical Society (pp. 8 and 9), Commander H. R. Hatfield RN (pp. 10, 11 and 12), Henry Brinton Esq (the colour half moon on p. 10), Novosti Press Agency (p. 24), UPI and AP News Agencies (pp. 28 to 33), and above all by The National Aeronautics and Space Administration (pp. 2 to 3, 7, 12, 13, 24 to 25, and 28 to 48), all of whom the publishers gratefully thank and acknowledge.

First published in the United States of America 1969
by Rand McNally & Company P O Box 7600, Chicago, Illinois U S A.
Library of Congress Catalog Card Number 73-94055
Visual Aids by DIAGRAM and Colin Rattray
Patrick Moore's *Moon Flight Atlas* was designed by Peter Kindersley and Melvyn Gill
Typesetting by James C. Joyce Ltd
Printed by Smeets Offset, Weert, Netherlands
Bound by Proost en Brandt N.V., Amsterdam